W9-ADY-895

STARCRAFT

IN 1609 GALILEO WAS ACCLAIMED BY DISTINGUISHED
CITIZENS OF VENICE WHEN HE DEMONSTRATED
HIS FIRST TELESCOPE FROM THE TOWER OF ST. MARKS

STARCRAFT

By WILLIAM H. BARTON, Jr.

Late Curator, Hayden Planetarium, New York

AND

JOSEPH MARON JOSEPH

Principal, Smedley Junior High School
Chester, Pennsylvania

New York   WHITTLESEY HOUSE   *London*

McGRAW-HILL BOOK COMPANY, INC.

523.8
B28S

28043
Sept '52

PUBLISHED BY WHITTLESEY HOUSE
A division of the McGraw-Hill Book Company, Inc.

Preface to the First Edition

With the increasing interest in observational astronomy, there has long been felt the need for guidance. Instructors in schools, leaders in activity clubs, guides in scout groups, and counselors in summer camps need a suitable book. The authors felt that none existed and, with the desire to fill this need, offer this volume to the interested reader.

No longer need star study be a mere reading course for the winter fireside, or a dull and uninteresting study of mathematics in the classroom. The young person seeking to know the world around him may, with the aid of the suggestions offered here, follow the paths that the pioneers of astronomy trod. Here he gets personal and direct experience with the methods used by the early skygazers. The apparatus used in this sky study can be made by any group of boys and girls under the supervision of their arts and crafts instructor. The more mechanically minded can no doubt do the same on their own initiative.

The equipment is inexpensive and should not tax the pocket money of ambitious youngsters. Many of the instruments may be made for group use and, if made carefully, will serve their purpose for a long while.

★ v ★

There is no limited season for sky study. Each month unfolds more of the ever-changing panorama of the heavens. Schooltime in winter and camp time in summer are both star time. Not all the work in astronomy is "night" work. During the day the sun offers much material for measurement and study. The sky shines alike over east and west, north and south. We never have to travel to see the stars. At home, at school, or in camp the sky above us is waiting for our eyes to see and for our minds to grasp its mystery and its wonders.

THE AUTHORS.

Preface to the Second Edition

SINCE the time of the first edition of this book, interest in observational astronomy has felt the quickening of the needs of global navigation. The late Professor William H. Barton's teaching and research in navigation at the Hayden Planetarium, especially in connection with his classes for midshipmen of the United States Navy, resulted in his devising a simplified method of navigation. This "thumbnail," or emergency, method is added to the second edition in order to give the reader an opportunity to practice a system of navigation that requires only a knowledge of observational astronomy and simple arithmetic.

For those camera fans who like to photograph nature, a short chapter has been included that teaches them how to take pictures of the night sky. Such pictures will be worthy additions to their nature study albums.

Grateful acknowledgment is here made to Dr. Peter van de Kamp, Professor of Astronomy and Director of the Sproul Observatory, Swarthmore College, Swarthmore, Pa., for his kindness in reviewing the new material in this edition.

J. M. J.

Contents

STARCRAFT

☆
★ I ★
☆

Starlight and Sky Sights

TWINKLING star lights have always caused man to look up and marvel at the beautiful sights in the night sky. On clear, dark nights everyone—young and old, savage and civilized—has had the same feeling, that if the arms were stretched up, he could touch the stars. When the poet Milton wrote in *Paradise Lost*, "Innumerable as the stars of the night," he believed, like most people today, that the sky twinkles with millions of stars! You may enjoy looking at the star-studded sky, but you should know that you can never touch one of those distant points of light. You will be surprised, also, at the number of stars that you can see and count (see Fig. 1).

The stars have been counted many times by famous astronomers. The average person with normal eyesight, at a place where the sky is dark, can count about 2,500 stars. If your eyes are especially keen, you can count about 3,000 stars. If you wear glasses and remove them, you will be able to count less than 2,500. Of course, if you own field glasses or a small telescope, you can see many more. With the 100-inch telescope at Mt. Wilson, Calif., astronomers can see and photograph about 1,000,000,000 stars. This number will be increased when the 200-inch telescope is finished and erected at Mt. Palomar, Calif. (see page 214).

Although the number of objects that we can see is a disappointment, the beauty of the bright, twinkling stars against the dark sky dome has been appreciated by people of all countries and of all times. It is an easy step from admiring the

Fig. 1.—Girls and boys pointing out stars in the sky.

beauty of the night to imagining and connecting the different stars into patterns. Perhaps you have formed figures with moving clouds. You may have done the same with the stars.

The ancient Babylonians, Romans, Greeks, and Egyptians, with their superstitious religions, saw the same sky that you see. They also formed imaginative patterns with the stars in the sky. To them, the different designs represented their heroes, their gods and goddesses, and their folk stories. We call these groups "constellations," which is a combination of two Latin words *con* meaning "together," and *stella*

★ 4 ★

meaning a "star." Thus, constellation means a group of fixed stars.

At present, we cannot say when or how these constellations were selected. The first reliable record of them came to us from

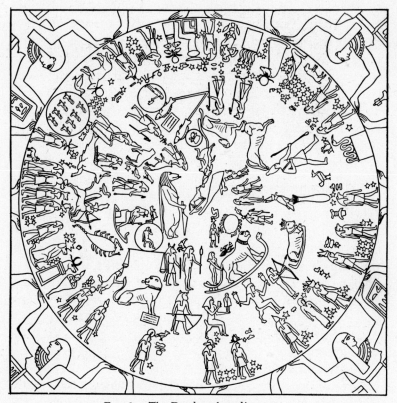

Fig. 2.—The Dendarrah zodiac stone.

the Egyptian, Ptolemy, who catalogued the stars and knew these figures. He gave us to understand that they were very old then, and that was more than 1,800 years ago. About 100 years ago, a stone was discovered in an Egyptian temple at Dendarrah (see Fig. 2) showing some of these figures just as we imagine them to be today. That stone is about 3,000 years old and was probably copied from one still older. So our

★ 5 ★

knowledge about the beginning of these groups is very small.

Ptolemy, the Egyptian astronomer, gave us 48 of these constellations and since then others have been added until there are now 88. At present, the names of the constellations are in Latin, but sometimes people prefer the use of words in their native language. Many years ago, a number of people tried to change these Roman mythological names to those of Biblical characters, but the other names had been used so long that it was not possible to change them.

When you look at the stars, therefore, you can imagine your own constellation figures, but it is better to keep the Latin names because they are known all over the world. The groups of stars forming Ursa Major is called the Big Bear in English, but any non-English-speaking astronomer in the world will know just what stars form Ursa Major.

Do not expect to see in the sky the figure corresponding to the name of the constellation, for you will be disappointed. Some few really do look like the animal or figure for which they are named, *but most do not*. It is difficult for us today to imagine how anyone could have given a star group its name. But it seems that in olden times these groups served as symbols and reminded people of some event or of some important person. Just as we build a monument or a bridge and call it for some great person, so the ancients named the star groups.

The Washington Monument in Washington, D. C., does not look anything like George Washington, but it stands as a symbol for him: straight, noble, plain, and upright. In the same way, Leo, the Lion, in the sky does not accurately resemble a lion (see Fig. 3, page 7), but when it was named, the sun was in that part of the sky in the summer, and the heat was as "fierce as a lion." Today we accept these names merely to save time and to have a common pattern which star-gazers all over the world will recognize.

The light from the stars in the different constellations gives us a beautiful sky sight, but we should remember that each

★ 6 ★

star is actually a large ball of bright, glowing, gaseous material. In simple words, each star in the night heavens is like our sun in that it gives light and heat. These sun-stars look to be so small because they are millions and millions of

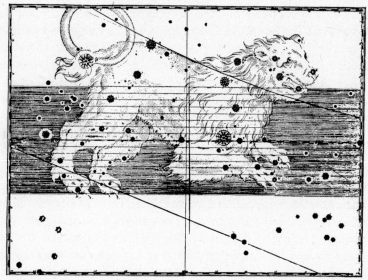

Fig. 3.—Constellation figure of Leo, from Bayer's *Uranometria*, 1603.

miles away. Later on you shall learn how far away these distant sun-stars are. We are too far away from them to feel their heat, but we can see their light even though they look like pin points.

Of the 9,000 such stars that we can see with the naked eye in the entire sky, there are about 500 bright ones which we can easily group into constellation figures. Of these, we can see about 200 or 250 at any one time. The ancient observers worked with a few hundred stars formed into convenient patterns. They called the rest "unformed"; that is, not included in the constellations. We shall consider them "unformed" also, and not bother with them—at least not until you have a telescope. This comparatively small number of stars makes constellation study easier.

★ 7 ★

Among the 500 objects in the night sky, there are five bright ones which do not seem to follow the regular constellation stars. The Greeks and Babylonians also noticed these five and observed them to move among the constellations. They called them "planets," which means "moving stars," in order to show the difference between them and the fixed stars in the constellation figures. The five planets which the ancient astronomers saw were called Mercury, Venus, Mars, Saturn, and Jupiter, after their gods and goddesses. They also considered the sun and the moon to be planets, and it was not until the seventeenth century that these two were properly understood to be different from the planets. Along the Mediterranean, there are temple ruins which were used as places of worship to these planet gods.

At the present time we know that there are nine planets (including the earth), although we can see only the five ancient ones with the naked eye. The others, Uranus, Neptune, and Pluto, must be observed through a telescope. The planets are dark, reflecting objects like the earth. We see them because the light from our sun is reflected back to us. Thus, the planets are enormous, mirrorlike globes, bouncing back the light from the sun to us on the earth. The planets are smaller than any but the smallest stars, but appear larger and brighter because they are thousands of times nearer to us than the nearest star.

When the bright moon is in the night sky, the fainter stars seem to fade away just as all the stars do when the sun is in the day sky. The moon is like the earth and the other eight planets; it is seen because it reflects the sunlight to us. The moon was called Luna by the Romans, and it was thought that its bright light caused people to become lunatics. Our word "month" originally came from the old Anglo-Saxon name for month, "moonth," meaning "of the moon." You shall learn more about the moon later.

Frequently, on clear dark nights, you may see what seems to be a star that darts rapidly a short distance across the sky and then vanishes. It looks like a Fourth of July firecracker burning in a rocket stream. These are popularly miscalled "shooting stars" but are known as "meteors" by astronomers. Meteors are not stars at all, but are small masses of iron, or stones about the size of sand grains, flying through space. They burn up when they hit the earth's atmosphere. Sometimes other sights are seen in the night skies. These may be comets, which sometimes look like stars with tails of faint light (see Fig. 1). Some comets are bright enough to be seen in broad daylight, but most require a telescope for observation.

With a telescope we can see odd things. Clusters are stars together in a swarm, but a long distance from the earth. Then there are great masses of luminous gas, like enormous clouds. These are nebulae. Scattered all over the sky are stars in pairs, called "double stars." Occasionally, certain stars change their brightness, some in a regular way, others unexpectedly. These are variable stars. A dim star that suddenly bursts into great brilliance and then soon fades out again is a "nova," or new star.

During the summer and autumn months, you may have seen a light cloudy band in the sky almost overhead. This is the Milky Way, or Galaxy. It is made up of billions of very distant stars which appear to the naked eye to form a wide, hazy, half-circle ribbon. Through the larger telescopes, we see each star as a tiny dot in this haze.

The answer to the question of what happens to the stars in the daytime bothered star gazers for a long time. The stories ancient people told about this were based on the idea that the world was flat. Some said the stars dipped into the ocean on the west to be washed and cleaned, and then moved under the water to be seen again at the eastern edge of the world. Others believed the stars went into caves and holes at the edge of the world, and then crept around the northern horizon to come up in the east at dawn. Today we know that these stories are not true.

★ 9 ★

If the sun did not make the sky so bright during the day, you could see the stars just as you do at night. The sunlight is spread out over the sky by the dusty air around the earth so that the sky appears brighter than the stars and they fade out. If there were no air around the earth, the day sky would be as black as the night sky. The sun would appear in it as a large spot like a very bright full moon, only much more brilliant. The one time you can seen the stars in the day is when the sun is hidden by the moon coming between it and the earth—an eclipse of the sun.

The daytime sky is filled with stars which we see at night during the opposite season of the year. Thus, the summer night constellations are overhead during the winter daytime, and the autumn constellations are in the sky during the spring daytime. The opposite of this is also true. Later on, when you have learned more about the constellations, you can tell which ones are overhead, but invisible, in the daytime. People who love the beauty of the starlit sky have noticed that the sky looks like a motion-picture screen going slowly from the eastern to the western horizon. Other stargazers have said that the night sky is like a dome rolling overhead, as if you were within a great ball and the stars were painted on the inside surface. All agree that the stars in the various constellations appear to rise in the east and set in the west, just as the sun does. Actually, of course, the stars do not move; they seem to do so, because of the earth's motion upon its axis, about which you learned in geography. The strange yet simple thing about the star groups is that they "move" in the same section of the sky every year and that they may be found in the same position at the same time every year. The sky, for the sake of convenience, has been divided into zones or roads over which the constellations travel. If you will remember these paths, it will aid you in studying the stars.

Excepting six constellations in a special place, which will be discussed separately, the star groups rise in the east and set in the west. They are then invisible to us for several months, when again the same constellations rise on the eastern horizon. Of course, if you wish to stay up the entire night, until the sun rises, you will be able to observe nearly all the constellations in one evening. We have divided the sky dome into four paths called: (*a*) circumpolar, (*b*) zodiacal, (*c*) northern, and (*d*) southern.

TABLE I

SKY PATHS OF THE CONSTELLATIONS

(The prominent constellations which appear in each sky path after twilight)

CIRCUMPOLAR PATH

	Ursa Major		Cassiopeia
	Ursa Minor		

ZODIACAL PATH

Spring	Cancer	*Autumn*	Capricornus
	Leo		Aquarius
	Virgo		Pisces
Summer	Libra	*Winter*	Aries
	Scorpius		Taurus
	Sagittarius		Gemini

NORTHERN PATH

Spring	Auriga	*Autumn*	Aquila
	Boötes		Cygnus
			Lyra
Summer	Hercules	*Winter*	Perseus
	Corona Borealis		Andromeda

SOUTHERN PATH

Spring	Canis Major	*Autumn*	Same as zodiac
Summer	Same as zodiac	*Winter*	Orion
			Canis Minor

The circumpolar path is a region around the northern part of the sky where the stars neither rise nor set, but go around counterclockwise. These, called "circumpolar stars," may be seen on any clear night in the year. This region will be described for those who live in the latitude of New York

★ 11 ★

(41° North), but will be nearly the same for use anywhere in the United States.

The zodiacal path covers the belt around the sky along which the sun, the moon, and the planets move. The zodiac is divided into 12 parts or signs, and there are 12 constellations having the same names as those signs. It is these 12 in which we are interested and three of these will be described for each season of the year; the three that are plainly visible early in the evening during that season.

The southern path covers the region between the zodiac and the southern horizon. This also will be taken up season by season. The northern or middle path lies between the circumpolar and the zodiacal zone and will be treated in the same way.

There are still a great many constellations below the southern horizon, but as we cannot see these stars in the United States, we shall not have anything to say about them.

ADVANCED READING ACTIVITY

Fath, E. A.: *Elements of Astronomy*. New York, McGraw-Hill Book Company, Inc., 1934.

Fisher, Clyde: *Exploring the Heavens*. New York, The Thomas Y. Crowell Company, 1937.

Lewis, Isabel: *Astronomy for Young People*. New York, Duffield & Green, Inc., 1922.

Newcomb, Simon: *Astronomy for Everybody*. Garden City, N. Y., Garden City Publishing Company, 1932. (Revised by R. H. Baker.)

Stokley, James: *Stars and Telescopes*. New York, Harper & Brothers, 1936.

White, W. B.: *Seeing Stars*. Cleveland, Ohio, Harter Publishing Company, 1935.

Wylie, C. C.: *Astronomy, Maps and Weather*. New York, Harper & Brothers, 1942.

II

Pointing to the Stars

IN THE first chapter you learned what was in the night sky; that the stars can be imagined to form patterns, called "constellations." They move in definite paths, going from the eastern horizon across the sky and then setting in the west. You have learned that the figures are formed with about 500 of the brighter stars, and that five of these are planets which move against the background of the stars. Yet it has been found that many observers have trouble in knowing where to look for the constellations without a teacher or a guide to show them.

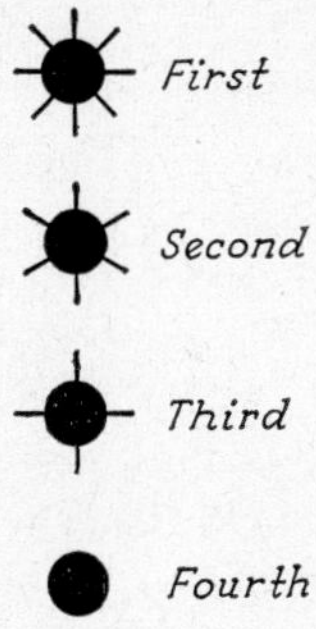

First

Second

Third

Fourth

FIG. 4.—Symbols for star charts.

This chapter has star charts which will show you where to point in the night sky to locate and identify any prominent constellation about 8 P.M. The constellations formed by the brighter stars will be described one at a time. The ancient stories from Greek mythology will be briefly mentioned. Important facts obtained by modern astronomy will be given. When you have learned where to point for the constellations, you can look for certain things which would be too small to be discovered by themselves. Many can be observed with the unaided eye, some with a pair of field glasses, and a few will require a telescope. You can buy a telescope, or you can make one cheaply by following the directions in Chapter IX.

In describing the constellations, some new words will be used. In order that you will understand the meanings of these terms, it is necessary to explain them.

1. *Magnitude*. The brightness of a star is described by a number. The bright stars were called "first magnitude" by the ancients. Another class, just dimmer than these, were said to be of the "second magnitude." Still dimmer ones were placed in the third, fourth, and fifth magnitudes, and so on. To indicate the stars of the different magnitudes, various distinctive symbols are shown on the charts. These are shown in the diagram (see Fig. 4).

2. *Star Distances*. The stars are so far away that it is not convenient to tell their distances in miles. A longer ruler is used and called a light-year. This is the distance light travels in one year, and is nearly 6,000,000,000,000 miles. The nearest star is 4.3 light-years distant, which means about 26,000,000,-000,000 miles. Its name is Proxima Alpha Centauri.

3. *Star Names*. The brighter stars have individual names. Most of these were given to them by the Arabs more than a thousand years ago, and described the place that the star marks in the figure. For instance, Rigel, in the foot of Orion, means the "foot."

4. *A Simple Way to Mark the Stars*. In 1603, Bayer, a German astronomer, made a famous set of star charts, and a part of one is shown in Fig. 3. To simplify the designations of the stars, he used a Greek letter for each star in a constellation instead of its Arabic name. It is easier to remember a letter than a long cumbersome name. For instance, he named Sheratan β Arietis, which means that it is the second brightest star in this constellation because β is the second letter in the Greek alphabet. He designated the brightest star in each constellation α, the next β, and so on. He did not use his plan consistently in all constellations. Table II will acquaint you with the names and appearance of the Greek letters.

TABLE II

THE GREEK ALPHABET

α	alpha	ι	iota	ρ	rho
β	beta	κ	kappa	σ	sigma
γ	gamma	λ	lambda	τ	tau
δ	delta	μ	mu	υ	upsilon
ϵ	epsilon	ν	nu	φ	phi
ζ	zeta	ξ	xi	χ	chi
η	eta	o	omicron	ψ	psi
θ	theta	π	pi	ω	omega

To use these charts correctly, you must (1) *be able to point to the north at night*, (2) be able to point to 16 points on the compass, and (3) be able to estimate the sky height of the constellation.

The 16 compass points may be learned by studying the horizon circle diagrams. The horizon circle may be formed by extending the arm to point at the place where the sky seems to meet the earth; turn around in a circle.

The sky height of the constellation may be measured if you point your arm to the horizon and then move it straight up until you are pointing overhead. You will notice that your arm has made a quarter circle from the horizon to overhead. For the purpose of pointing to the constellations, this quarter circle is divided into four parts, as shown in Fig. 5. It is

Fig. 5.—Estimating sky heights.

suggested that you practice pointing to the true north, to different compass points, and to the sky height. When you can do this quickly and easily, you are ready to use the following constellation charts.

DIRECTIONS

(1) Turn to the page of the constellation that you wish to find.
(2) Pick out the compass point which is connected to the correct
month of the year; (3) point in that direction; (4) raise your arm
to the approximate height of the shadow figure. With your extended
arm in that position, you will be pointing to the constellation you
want. For example, suppose you wanted to know where to look
for Perseus at 8 P.M. and the date was March 1. Follow the steps
shown above. (1) Turn to page 68 where Perseus is described;
(2) examine the compass to find where March is printed. Estimate
this direction; in this case, it will be the Northwest; (3) point your
arm in that direction; (4) raise your pointed arm to the height
shown by the arm of the little man; (5) you will be pointing to
about the center of the constellation of Perseus; (6) examine the
right-hand chart showing the stars making up Perseus, or use your
sky charts as described in Chapter III; (7) look up at the section
of the sky where your arm is pointing; compare the stars to the chart.

In case you do not find the correct month printed on the
compass lines, the constellation is *not* visible on that date
for that time.

The charts in this chapter are out of proportion to the
actual size of the constellations. Thus, Ursa Major and Orion
are much larger than the diagrams indicate. It was necessary
to do this, because the size of the book did not permit all
constellations to be drawn in exact scale. You should be
careful, therefore, when you are pointing to the constellation,
to remember that it may be many times larger than the
drawing looks.

These pointing directions have been drawn for 8 P.M.
Standard Time. If you are observing at 10 P.M., go to the next
later month on the compass. In the winter, if you are observing
at 6 P.M., pick out the pointing directions given for one month
previous. In general, there will be about a *half month change*
for each hour's difference before or after 8 P.M.

On many pages of constellation study will be found a photograph of some object in that star field which is so dim that no ordinary telescope will reveal it with sufficient clearness. Study these as you would through the eyepiece of a great telescope. Their places among the stars are marked with ☐. On many of the captions for the telescope pictures you will find a reference to Messier's catalogue. For instance, a nebula or cluster will be numbered 13 in Messier's catalogue, or merely marked M13. This refers to a book written by Charles Messier in 1781. This French amateur astronomer was a comet hunter and made himself this famous list of 103 objects that looked like comets but were really bright masses of gas or great clusters of stars.

In the same way N.G.C. refers to New General Catalog, a much larger book of these same objects that Messier listed. It was published in 1887 by the Royal Astronomical Society of England.

MYTHOLOGY OF THE
CIRCUMPOLAR CONSTELLATIONS

AN OLD Greek story relates how Juno had Callisto, of whom she was jealous, turned into a bear. Callisto's son Arcas met his mother one day when he was hunting. She was so changed that he did not recognize her. She came near him and he was about to shoot her with an arrow, when Jupiter picked them both up quickly and placed them in the sky as Ursa Major and Ursa Minor.

Cassiopeia, in another old Greek tale, was the queen of an imaginary land called Aethiopia. Her husband was King Cepheus (see Chart 1, page 82). The queen boasted of her beauty and offended the sea nymphs. They begged Neptune to send a sea monster, Cetus (Chart 2, page 83), to ravage the coast of that country. The oracle directed Cepheus to chain his daughter, Andromeda (page 70) to the rocks, so Cetus might devour her. Perseus (page 68), returning from slaying the Medusa, saw the plight of Andromeda and came to her rescue. For that reason he is often called the Hero.

Draco, the Dragon (Chart 1, page 82), is often recognized as the one Hercules (page 58) slew. This dragon guarded the golden apples in the Garden of Hesperides. The slaying of the dragon was the eleventh labor of Hercules.

Camelopardalis is one of the newer star groups and is not shown on any of our charts. The name means Giraffe. This constellation was devised in 1614 by Bartschius. The stars are all very dim so we do not list it among the important groups for observation.

CONSTELLATIONS ALONG THE CIRCUMPOLAR PATH

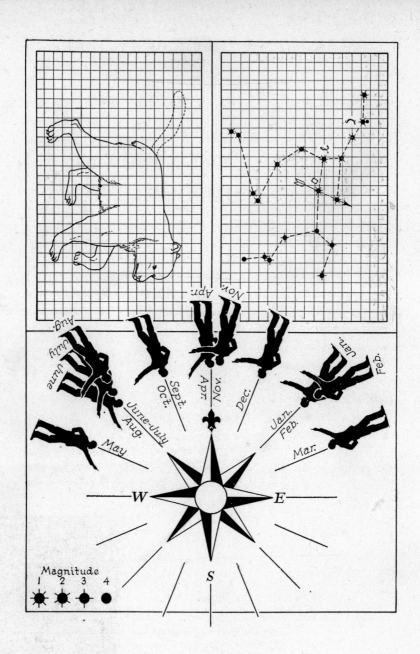

URSA MAJOR—THE GREAT BEAR

THE great bear is famous as being the home of the Big Dipper, the best-known group of stars in the Northern Hemisphere. These stars were a bear to the North American Indians. The four stars in the bowl were the bear, the three in the handle were hunters. The first hunter carried the bow and arrow, the second, the pot to cook the bear in. If you look close you can see an extra star (Alcor) near Mizar, ζ Ursae Majoris. The last one in the handle is the hunter with sticks to light the fire. Alcor was known to the Arabs as a test of eyesight for entrance into their army.

With the Naked Eye. The stars at the end of the bowl are the Pointers and a line through them leads you to the polestar (see the arrow). Study Alcor and Mizar. Mizar is about second magnitude. Alcor is 72 light-years away and 11 times as bright as the sun.

With the Opera Glass. Study the pairs of stars that make the feet of the bear, and you will see beautiful fields of dim stars. Look at Alcor and Mizar and notice how far apart they seem. They are 11 minutes (11′) apart and are not really a double star, but Mizar itself is double, and so is Alcor.

With the Telescope. Between Alcor and Mizar is a faint star that was mistaken for a planet nearly 200 years ago (what could a planet be doing here?) and named Sidus Ludovicianum. Study the field near γ Ursae Majoris. Mizar is of magnitudes 2 and 4, distance 14 seconds (14″).

OWL NEBULA IN URSA MAJOR

A large, pale planetary nebula that looks like the face of an owl. Stars form the eyes and nose on the owl's face. The nebula is dimly glowing gas, probably illuminated by the stars inside it, like fog around a street lamp. In Messier's catalogue it is No. 97. This beautiful photograph of the Owl Nebula was made at Lick Observatory on Mt. Hamilton, Calif.

★ 21 ★

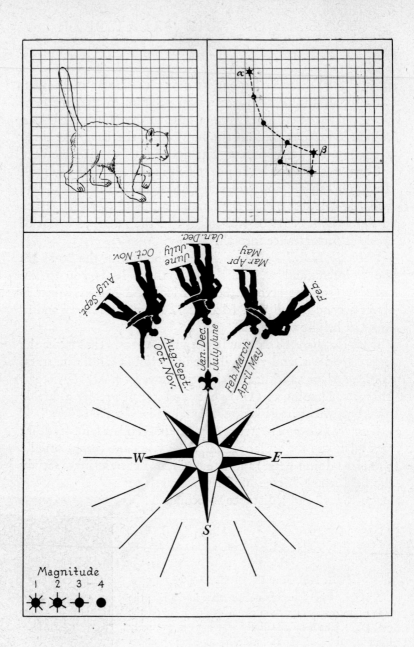

Magnitude
1 2 3 4

★ 22 ★

URSA MINOR—THE LITTLE BEAR

THIS important constellation includes the polestar, vari-
ously called Polaris or the North Star. It is very close
to the north pole of the sky. This point is just over the North
Pole of the earth and therefore is fixed in its position on the
sky. The polestar is almost fixed, and to the *naked eye* it is
always in the same spot. It points out the north and by
measuring its height above the horizon we can find out our
latitude (see Chapter V). Polaris is at the end of the handle
of the Little Dipper. The two stars at the end of the bowl of
the dipper are the Guardians. They circle around the pole
closer than any other bright stars.

With the Naked Eye. Trace out the Dipper and notice how it
pours into the Big Dipper. Find the Pole. Notice the difference
in color between α Ursae Minoris, Polaris, and β Ursae
Minoris, Kochab. Polaris is yellowish white and the other is
red.

With the Opera Glass. If you have a good field glass, you can
catch a glimpse of the ninth magnitude companion to Polaris.

With the Telescope. Polaris is a double star of magnitudes
2 and 9, distance 18″. Polaris is 465 light-years away and is
2,500 times as brilliant as our sun.

THE POLESTAR IN URSA MINOR

The polestar was not always so near the north
pole of the sky. The diagram shows that the
pole of the sky goes around a circle among the
stars in about 26,000 years. Five thousand years
ago Thuban was the polestar and 12,000 years
from now Vega will be near the pole of the sky.
The cause of this is too long a story to tell here.

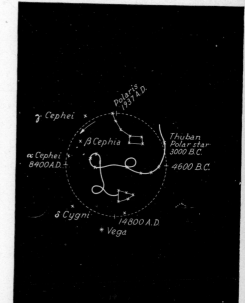

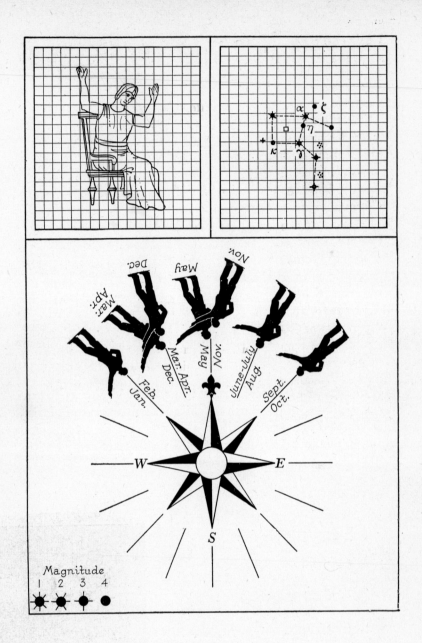

Magnitude
1 2 3 4

CASSIOPEIA—THE LADY IN THE CHAIR

★

CASSIOPEIA might better be called the Queen on the Throne. The most conspicuous figure in the group is the W- or M-shaped figure. Cassiopeia is just across the pole from the Great Dipper. Both are circumpolar constellations, so when one is high in the sky the other is low over the north point. Near κ Cassiopeiae, a nova, or new star, appeared in 1572 and was seen and studied by Tycho Brahe. It is often spoken of as Tycho's Star. It is marked here by ✕.

With the Naked Eye. Trace out the W and find κ Cassiopeiae, near which Tycho's Star appeared. For a while this was the brightest star in the sky, even exceeding Sirius. Find α Cassiopeiae (Schedar). This star is slightly variable, and it is 191 light-years away.

With the Opera Glass. ζ Cassiopeiae—near it is a little circlet that looks like a small corona, or crown. Study the beautiful star sights near and between γ Cassiopeiae and κ Cassiopeiae.

With the Telescope. η Cassiopeiae is a double star of fourth and eighth magnitudes; 10″ apart; colors, green and purple. Herschel discovered this in 1779.

Schedar is double, of second and ninth magnitudes, 1′ apart.

Look for the clusters marked ∵∴

UNIFORM FIELD IN MILKY WAY IN CASSIOPEIA

This field in the Milky Way has the stars scattered somewhat evenly. This is an unusual and striking field of stars. Generally, the stars are bunched in clouds and clusters. This picture is near κ Cassopeiae, which you can find on the chart. The picture was made at the Yerkes Observatory. The plate was exposed 8 hours and 46 minutes in the great telescope.

★ 25 ★

MYTHOLOGY OF THE
ZODIACAL CONSTELLATIONS

CANCER, the Crab, was put in the sky by Juno as a reward for biting the foot of Hercules while he was killing Hydra (Chart 2, page 83), the Water Snake. Juno was an enemy of Hercules.

Leo is the Nemean lion that Hercules slew in the first of his twelve labors.

Virgo's story is not very clear. Libra, the Scales, was once associated with Julius Caesar as the scales of justice.

Scorpius is said to have caused Orion's (page 78) death by stinging him, so they were placed in opposite parts of the sky. One rises when the other sets.

Sagittarius is sometimes associated with Chiron, who taught Hercules to use the bow and arrow.

Capricornus does not seem to have a very clear history.

Aquarius is the water carrier and may have been associated by the Babylonians with the rainy season.

Pisces, the Fishes, may have two members so we could represent an extra month occasionally put into the calendar by the Babylonians.

Aries, the Ram, represents the ram of the golden fleece mentioned in Greek mythology.

Taurus, the Bull, according to the Greek myth, represents Jupiter who changed himself into a white bull and carried away on his back the maiden Europa.

Gemini, the Twins, brothers of Helen of Troy, were on the way to the Trojan War when a storm arose. Orpheus played his harp (Lyra, page 66) and quelled the storm. Stars descended from the sky and settled over the heads of the twins. Thus they became the patron saints of seafaring people.

CONSTELLATIONS ALONG
THE ZODIACAL PATH

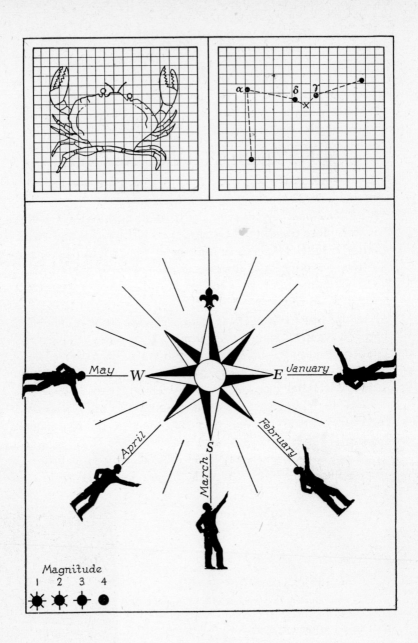

Magnitude
1 2 3 4

CANCER—THE CRAB

THIS zodiacal constellation is the dimmest of the twelve. Many years ago the sun was in this region when it was farthest north of the equator, and the days in the Northern Hemisphere are longest. Because of the "wobbling" of the earth's axis, this has now moved into Gemini. But we still call the line on the earth where the sun shines overhead at noon on June 22, the Tropic of Cancer.

With the Naked Eye. In the midst of this constellation are two stars close together. δ Cancri, the southern of these two, is fairly bright. This star is almost on the ecliptic. Between the two is a faint hazy spot—a cluster of many stars called Praesepe. Sometimes it is called the Beehive or Manger, marked ✕ on the map.

With the Opera Glass. Study Praesepe and notice how many stars you see in this famous group. Galileo studied this group carefully, mapping and counting the stars. Ptolemy records Jupiter passing over this cluster, the first scientific observation on Jupiter. Halley's comet was first seen near here in 1531.

With the Telescope. Study the Beehive more carefully. You can probably count over 300 stars in it. The moon frequently passes over (occults) γ Cancri. *This is an interesting thing to observe.* Study the cluster which is near α Cancri. Herschel found over 200 stars in it. How many can you see?

BEEHIVE CLUSTER IN CANCER

The famous cluster, Praesepe, is very beautiful in a small telescope. Large instruments have a field so small that you cannot appreciate the beauty of this group as well as you can in a fine photograph. This photograph, made by Barnard by exposing a plate for over 3 hours in the 10-inch telescope at Yerkes Observatory, shows the remarkable groupings of the stars in this cluster. In Messier's catalogue it is No. 44.

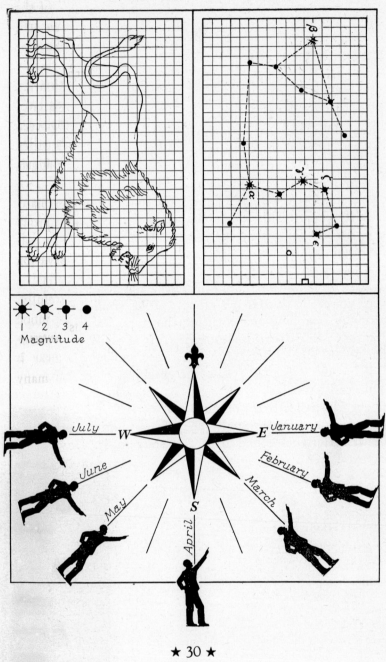

LEO—THE LION

THIS is one of the constellations of the zodiac and many years ago marked the place in the sky where the sun was at the hottest part of the summer and then shone "fierce as a lion." The figure consists of the "sickle" at the western end of the constellation forming the head and fore part of the lion, and a triangle marking the hindquarters.

With the Naked Eye. Regulus, α Leonis, is the bright star at the end of the handle of the sickle. Copernicus named it. With Antares, Aldebaran, and Fomalhaut, it is one of the four Royal Stars of Persia. Sometimes it is called the Lion's Heart. It is 59 light-years away. Denebola, β Leonis, is the tip of the Lion's tail. It is 43 light-years away.

With the Opera Glass. α Leonis is a double, ζ Leonis is a quadruple star.

With the Telescope. γ Leonis is the finest double in the northern sky; magnitudes 2 and 4; distance apart 4″; colors, yellow and green. Distance away is 136 light-years. α Leonis has a deep blue companion; magnitude 8; distance away 8′. A nebula in line with the two stars at the end of the blade of the sickle is marked ○.

SPIRAL NEBULA IN LEO

In order to photograph this universe of millions of stars the plate was exposed for 4 hours in the great 100-inch telescope at Mt. Wilson Observatory. The light from such a distant spiral nebula is so faint that we cannot see it but on the sensitive picture plate the light builds up a picture that we can see. Notice the spiral arms flying out from the main body of the nebula. If we could go away out in space our star system, or Galaxy, would look the same. This is designated N.G.C. 2903–05.

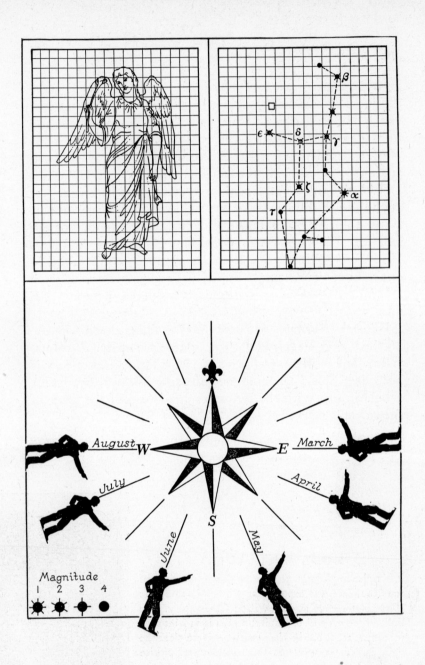

Magnitude
1 2 3 4

VIRGO—THE VIRGIN

THIS constellation has been named in many countries for the Goddess of the Harvest.

With the Naked Eye. Spica, α Virginis—a beautiful white star of the first magnitude, which, with Denebola, Arcturus, and Cor Caroli (in Canes Venatici), forms the Diamond in Virgo. Spica is 204 light-years away. Around the head and shoulders of Virgo is the Field of the Nebulae where more than 300 of these remote objects were discovered by Herschel. The sun is not far from β Virginis on September 23—the autumnal equinox.

With the Opera Glass. Observe the beautiful color of Spica which is more than 1,000 times as bright as the sun.

With the Telescope. γ Virginis is a famous double star with a period of 180 years. Each star is about third magnitude, 6″ apart. τ Virginis is a double star, magnitudes 4 and 9, distance more than 1′ apart. Look for the nebulae in the Field of the Nebulae.

SIDE VIEW OF NEBULA IN VIRGO

Most of the stars that we see on a starry night belong to "our" system. The sun and millions of other stars, like a great number of bees, form a round, flat swarm. There are millions of such swarms, or systems, but powerful telescopes are needed to see and photograph them. Many are shaped like two saucers with their rims together. This star system has its saucer rims turned toward our earth, and we see it edgewise. In the New General Catalog it is No. 5746. This picture was made by exposing a plate in the great 60-inch telescope at Mt. Wilson Observatory for 6 hours.

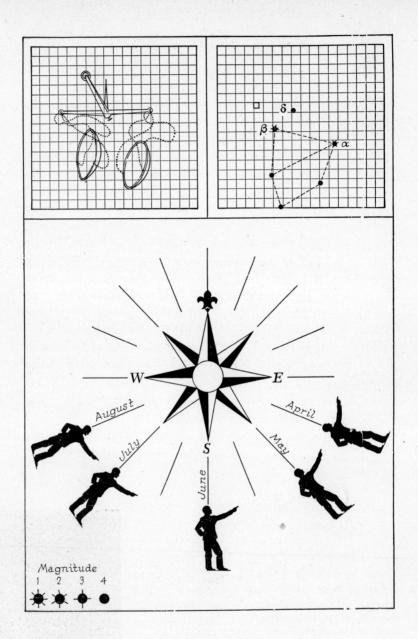

Magnitude
1 2 3 4

LIBRA—THE SCALES

Tʜɪs constellation was once a part of Scorpius, forming the claws of the Scorpion. The autumnal equinox was once here and the days and nights "balance" at that season.

With the Naked Eye. α Librae, "Zuben el genubi" as the Arabs called it, means the southern claw and is almost on the ecliptic. β Librae, "Zuben es schamali," means northern claw. This star is the only green star that you can see without a telescope.

With the Opera Glass. α Librae—this is a nice double for an opera or field glass. Magnitudes 3 and 6, and of a yellow and gray color. β Librae—the glass will make the green color easier to see and in addition will show a companion star near it which has a light blue color.

With the Telescope. Examine more closely α Librae and β Librae and study the colors of these interesting stars. δ Librae, just northwest of β Librae is a short-period variable star changing from 4.8 to 6.2 magnitude in a cycle of about 2.3 days. This is really a twin sun. One star going about the other and sometimes cutting down the light, like Algol, the most famous star of this type. (See Perseus.)

GLOBULAR CLUSTER IN LIBRA

This globular cluster of stars is one of about a hundred such objects in the whole sky. Considering the millions of stars, thousands of nebulae and even many more island universes, these star clusters are really rare. It requires a fairly large telescope to see the stars and a picture to bring out the beauty of the group. The cluster is so far away that the light takes 35,000 years to reach us. Therefore, we see it as it was more than 35,000 years ago. It is known as Messier No. 5. The photograph was made at Yerkes Observatory at Williams Bay, Wis.

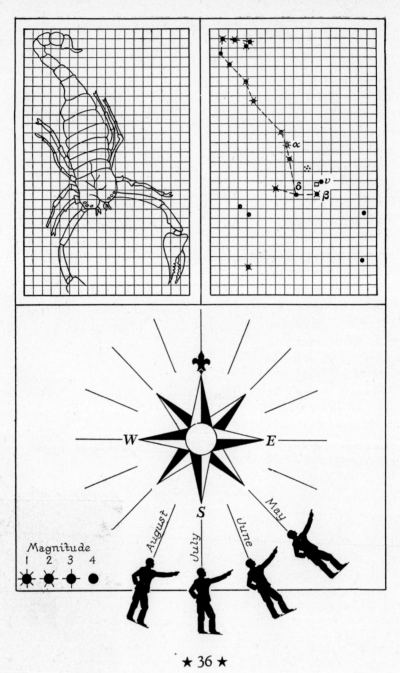

Magnitude
1 2 3 4

W E

August July June May

S

★ 36 ★

SCORPIUS—THE SCORPION

Scorpius is a group of the zodiac, yet very little of the sun's path lies within its bounds, less than in any other zodiacal constellation. On the opposite part of the sky from Orion, these stars are as conspicuous in the summer sky as Orion is in the winter.

With the Naked Eye. Antares, α Scorpii, is a bright red star. The name means Rival of Mars (Anti-Ares). Ares was the Greek name for Mars and they do look something alike. Its diameter is 390,000,000 miles. It is a first magnitude star and its distance is 163 light-years. It is really more than 700 times brighter than the sun. It is one of the four Royal Stars of Persia. Notice the pair of stars at the end of the Scorpion's tail. These represent the "sting."

With the Opera Glass. Antares—study the brilliant red color of this sun. No other star has just this color. Study the region near Antares for many dim stars in interesting figures. Some are double and triple.

With the Telescope. About midway between α Scorpii and β Scorpii is one of the finest clusters in the sky and is marked ∴. β Scorpii is a double star, of magnitudes 2 and 4, distance 13″. ν Scorpii is a fine quadruple star. Perhaps you will see only two stars about 41″ apart, of magnitudes 4 and 7.

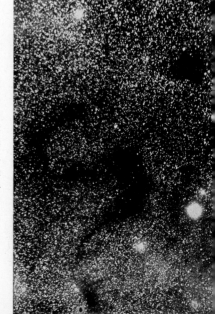

DARK NEBULA IN OPHIUCHUS

Not far from the constellation Scorpius is this dark S-shaped nebula. There are similar spots in Scorpius but they are not quite so striking in appearance as this field. These dark nebulae are really great clouds of dust or gas, cold and dark. They cut off the view of stars farther away just as a cloud blots out the moon on a cloudy night. This beautiful picture was taken with the great 100-inch telescope at Mt. Wilson Observatory on July 4, 1921, by the astronomer Barnard.

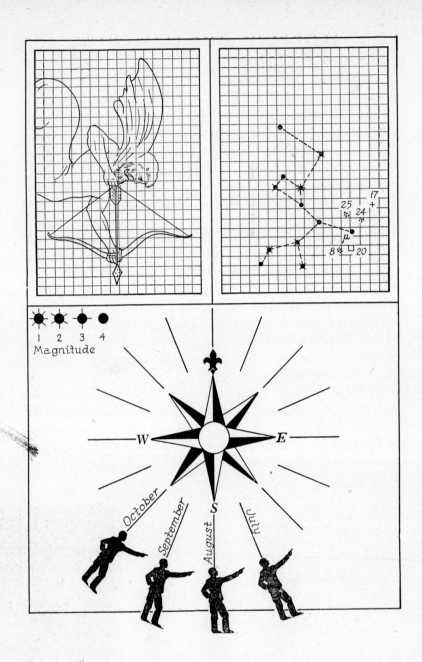

Magnitude

1 2 3 4

17
+
25 24
μ
8 ☐ 20

W   E

October   September   August   S   July

SAGITTARIUS—THE ARCHER

This zodiacal group is the one farthest south and is buried in the richest part of the Milky Way. Here the great star clouds light the sky in a broad and irregular belt. Many globular clusters are in this region also. The sun is in this constellation on December 22, the shortest day in our year. The mythology of this group is not so clear but it represents a centaur, half man and half horse, shooting an arrow from a drawn bow.

With the Naked Eye. Notice the dipper called the Little Milk Dipper in Sagittarius, probably because it is close to the Milky Way. Trace out the teapot—a very plain figure. Two clusters are marked M24 and M25 and you can see these without any field or opera glasses.

With the Opera Glass. Study carefully the clusters mentioned above and M8. John Herschel studied this carefully at his observatory at the Cape of Good Hope. Hunt for, and you will discover, many other clusters and nebulae.

With the Telescope. In addition to studying more carefully the fine clusters noted above, look for the two nebulae M20 (Trifid) marked □, and M17 (Horseshoe). μ is a triple star and you can perhaps separate its components, whose magnitudes are 3, 9, and 10 and are separated by 40″ and 45″.

TRIFID NEBULA IN SAGITTARIUS

One of the most beautiful of the gaseous clouds is the one in Sagittarius known as the Trifid Nebula, because it is split into three parts. To the eye it is only a dimly luminous cloud, but in a photograph, like this one taken with the great 100-inch telescope at Mt. Wilson, all the fine dark lanes are brought out. The light to take this photograph traveled across space from the Trifid for 2,000 years.

★ 39 ★

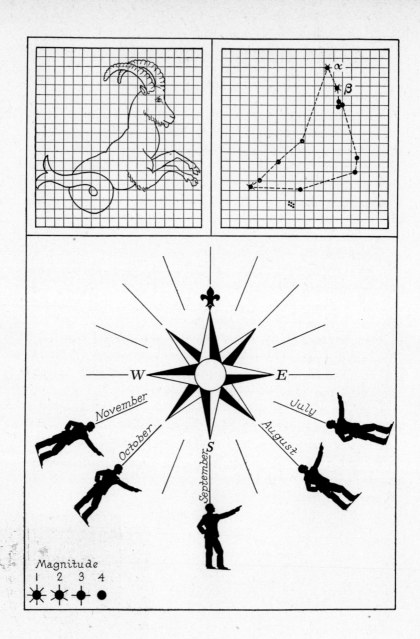

CAPRICORNUS—THE SEA GOAT

THIS constellation of the zodiac is not easily picked out as its stars are dim. They range along the sun's path, and many years ago the sun was here about December 23, at the winter solstice. Then it is farthest south of the equator, but that point has moved into Sagittarius, the next constellation.

After this date the sun begins climbing the sky again, climbing like a "goat." The line on the earth where the sun is just overhead at noon on this date is still called the Tropic of Capricorn.

With the Naked Eye. You can just see that α Capricorni and β Capricorni are doubles. Just below β Capricorni is a beautiful little group of dim stars. The stars forming α are about 6′ apart and those in β Capricorni nearly 4′ apart.

With the Opera Glass. Study the two stars at α Capricorni. They are not parts of a true double star, but are drifting apart rapidly. The ancients make no mention of the double because they were too close to be seen, except as one star. β Capricorni is a beautiful double—one star being blue and of magnitude 6 and the other yellow and of magnitude 2½.

With the Telescope. α Capricorni—each star noted above is a double. A very beautiful sight. Cluster M30 is very interesting, but hard to see in great detail. It is marked on the chart thus ∵

SUN SPOTS

Frequently the surface of the sun is marred by spots as this Yerkes Observatory photograph shows. These dark spots are great electrical storms in the hot atmosphere of the sun, and they affect the earth, producing aurora, disturbing the compass needle, and bothering the radio and telegraph. Capricornus is along the sun's path in the sky, but of course, when the sun is in this constellation we cannot see the stars that form it.

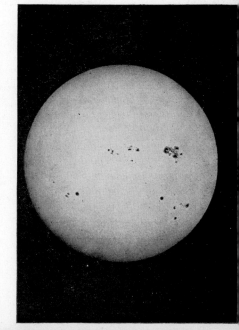

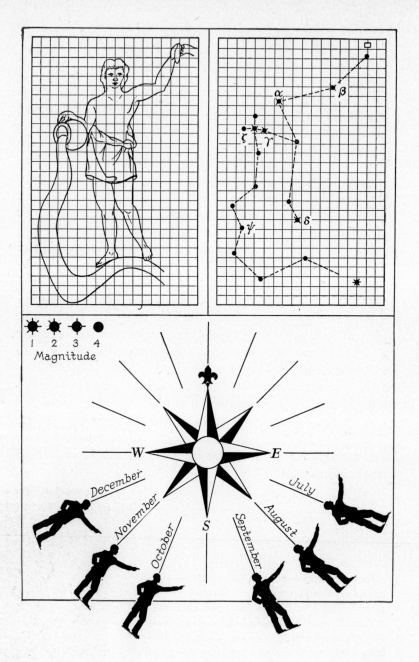

Magnitude
1 2 3 4

W E

December
July
November
October
September
August
S

★ 42 ★

AQUARIUS—THE WATER CARRIER

THE most conspicuous star figure in this zodiacal constellation is a group of four stars—the Y in Aquarius. This marks the water jug from which the water carrier is pouring water into the mouth of the southern fish (a strange pastime!). The other stars are not easily described.

With the Naked Eye. Find the Y, the water jug, and note the line of stars running south to Fomalhaut. This irregular line is a Water Stream. Fomalhaut is at the mouth of the Southern Fish. Not far from δ Aquarii, Tobias Mayer almost discovered the planet Uranus in 1766, but he thought it was a star.

With the Opera Glass. Study the stream of stars representing the flowing water. You will find many interesting groups.

With the Telescope. ζ Aquarii in the middle of the Y is a double star of a green color, magnitudes 4 and 4, almost 4″ apart. Ψ Aquarii is a double of magnitudes 4½ and 8, 50″ apart, and colors yellow and blue. □ is a beautiful nebula.

PLANETARY NEBULA IN AQUARIUS

A "planetary" nebula has nothing to do with planets, but it does look something like the disk of a planet in a small telescope. Sir William Herschel discovered this one in Aquarius and listed it in his catalogue of nebulae and clusters. It is pale blue in color and seems bright for this kind of an object. The Earl of Rosse many years ago first saw those two streamers coming out from the rim of the disk. This picture was made with the great 60-inch telescope at Mt. Wilson Observatory. It is designated as N.G.C. No. 7009.

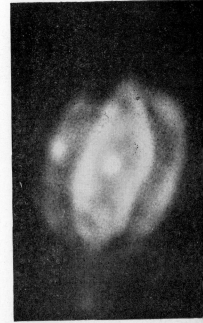

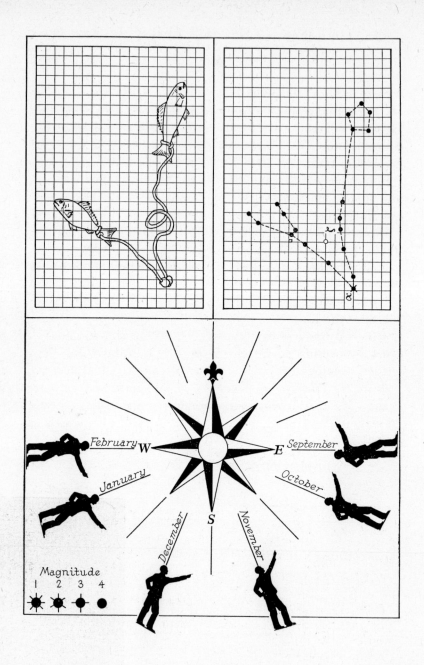

Magnitude
1 2 3 4

PISCES—THE FISHES

THIS zodiacal constellation is a long one and now contains the vernal equinox. The old figure shows two fishes with tails tied together by a long string, sometimes known as the Flaxen Cord. There are no bright stars in this group, but many dim ones. It was in this constellation that the triple conjunction of Mars, Jupiter, and Saturn took place in 6 B.C., and some connect this striking combination of planets with the Star of Bethlehem.

With the Naked Eye. The circlet of stars that is small and under the Square of Pegasus is the Western Fish. A long stream running southeast connects with a line running north to the Northern Fish. At the junction is the brightest star in the group, Al Rischa, α Piscium, a name given it by the Arabs meaning the Knot.

With the Opera Glass. Follow the circlets and the lines of stars connecting them and note the many beautiful little groups of faint stars that you cannot see with the naked eye.

With the Telescope. Al Rischa is a fine double; magnitudes 3 and 4; 3″ apart; colors, green and blue. ζ Piscium is a double of magnitudes 4 and 5, spaced 24″ apart. Hunt for a nebula at the place marked ◯.

SPIRAL NEBULA IN PISCES

The spiral nebula in this constellation is so dim that it was necessary to expose the plate for 5 hours in the 60-inch telescope at Mt. Wilson Observatory. These great celestial pin wheels are numbered by thousands in the sky. They are not gaseous, but are composed of millions of stars, whole universes, or star systems, so far away that the light requires millions of years to travel the gap between us. All but a few require great telescopes to see them, or study them. It is No. 74 in Messier's catalogue.

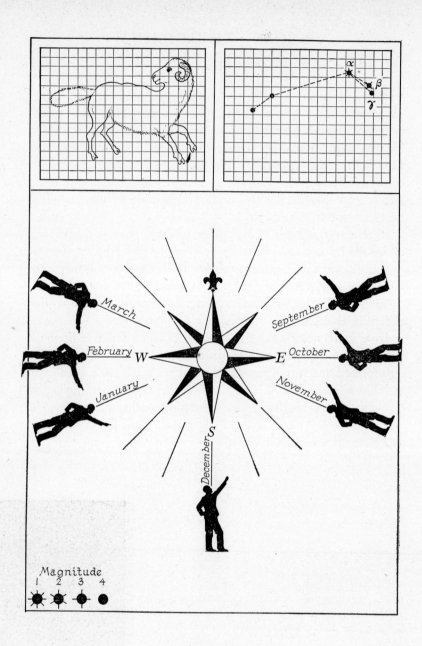

Magnitude
1 2 3 4

★ 46 ★

ARIES—THE RAM

Aries is generally given as the first sign of the zodiac. One explanation is that in the country where the zodiac was divided, the lamb was the first animal born in the springtime. The sun, many years ago, was near this point of the zodiac at the beginning of spring.

With the Naked Eye. There are no conspicuous stars in this small group. Notice the triangle of stars in the Ram's head. The brightest star α Arietis is named Hamal, and β Arietis is called Sheratan, and is 49 light-years away.

With the Opera Glass. This group offers very little for study with opera or field glass except to make the stars brighter. Hamal is a star much like our sun and is 81 light-years away.

With the Telescope. γ Arietis is a double star and was one of the first ones discovered. It was seen first by Robert Hooke in 1664 while he was watching a comet in this part of the sky. The stars are of the fourth magnitude and are 8″ apart; one is violet and the other yellow.

CONJUNCTION OF THREE PLANETS

Across the background of the dim stars in this constellation the planets move. Their paths lie almost in a line across the sky. Since they all move with different speeds, they must pass one another once in a while. Just as one of these neighbor worlds catches up with another they are said to be in conjunction. On January 8, 1921, three planets, Venus, Mars, and Uranus, were in conjunction in this part of the sky. This photograph made at Yerkes Observatory shows them as they looked on that rare occasion. Venus is the brightest and Uranus the dimmest.

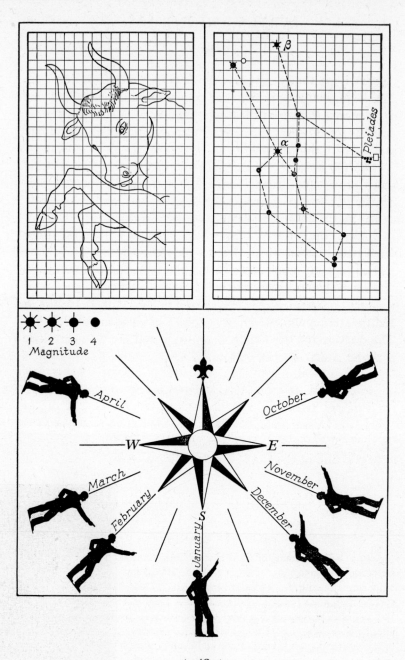

Magnitude
1 2 3 4

April
October
W
E
March
November
February
December
S
January

Taurus is the second constellation in the zodiac, Aries, the Ram, being the first. The group is a very important one. It contains the bright star, Aldebaran, and two clusters.

With the Naked Eye. Aldebaran, α Tauri, means the Follower and is 57 light-years away. It is pale red in color and is one of the four Royal Stars of Persia along with Regulus, Antares, and Fomalhaut. The Hyades is a V-shaped group of stars beginning near Aldebaran, forming the face of the bull. These stars really form a cluster moving through the sky. The Pleiades, this compact little dipper, is another distinct cluster generally classed as an "open cluster." Some see only six, others up to ten stars. It is sometimes called the Seven Sisters. The moon frequently eclipses Aldebaran.

With the Opera Glass. El Nath, the Tip, β Tauri, is a beautiful white star—pure white—and is 93 light-years away. Notice the delicate red color of Aldebaran. The Hyades is a beautiful field of stars. The V-shaped figure is somewhat broken up because you can see so many faint stars. Look for many pairs of stars. Look at the beautiful field of stars in the Pleiades.

With the Telescope. Look for the same objects you can see with the opera or field glass. Many more stars can be seen in the clusters and they shine more brilliantly. O marks the position of the Crab Nebula.

THE PLEIADES IN TAURUS

In these two pictures of the Pleiades one can see how the photograph will build up a picture by long exposure. In one picture the camera was open for 6 minutes and in the other for 600 minutes (10 hours). Notice how many more objects appear on one plate than on the other. Our eyes get tired if we look too long and we see less and less. The photographic film does not, but sees more and more. This picture was made at Yerkes Observatory.

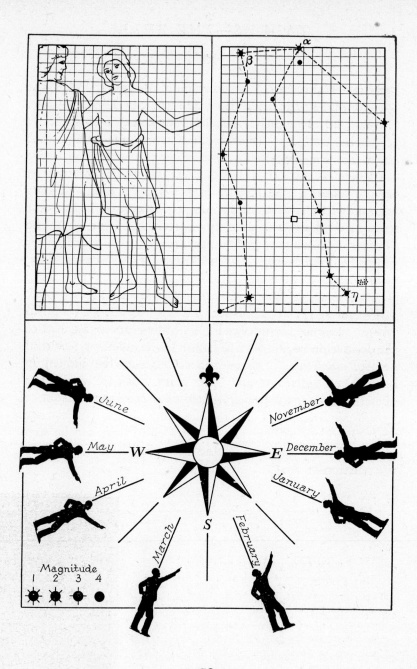

GEMINI—THE TWINS

Two bright stars, Castor and Pollux, mark this group. Gemini is a zodiacal group and the summer solstice is in it. In 1781, Herschel discovered the planet Uranus in this constellation, and in 1930, Clyde Tombaugh found Pluto in it (see Chapter VI).

With the Naked Eye. α Geminorum, Castor, the northern star of the twins, is a beautiful white star of 1.6 magnitude. This star is 44 light-years away and is a double star. One component is 25 and the other is 12 times as bright as the sun. Pollux, β Geminorum, the southern twin, is of magnitude 1.2 and is yellow. It is 33 light-years away and 29 times as bright as the sun.

With the Opera Glass. Near η Geminorum is a beautiful compact cluster that you can just see with a field glass or good opera glass as a tiny speck. Search the lower part of the constellation near the Milky Way for beautiful star fields.

With the Telescope. Castor is a double star, the finest in the sky, of magnitudes 2 and 3, 4″ apart, both white. Examine cluster near η. Notice the red star near the cluster.

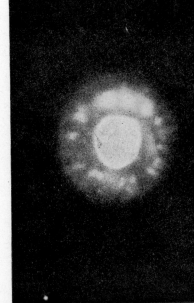

PLANETARY NEBULA IN GEMINI

This planetary nebula in Gemini was observed many years ago by Sir William Herschel. Through small telescopes hazy spots like this glowing gas look very much like comets when they are so far away that you cannot see the tail. Quite often when someone "discovers" a comet, it turns out to be an object like this. One has to be very careful that he does not make such a mistake. This photograph was made with the 5-foot telescope at Mt. Wilson Observatory. The nebula is No. 2392 in the N.G.C.

★ 51 ★

MYTHOLOGY OF THE CONSTELLATIONS IN THE NORTHERN PATH

AURIGA was said to have been a cripple and to have invented the chariot, but the story does not seem to fit into any myth.

Boötes, the Bear Driver, follows the Great Bear around the sky. Since the Big Dipper is called the Wagon in some countries, Boötes is often called the Wagoner.

Hercules was the great-grandson of Perseus and Andromeda. He performed the "twelve labors" that are described in mythology. Some believe the twelve constellations are connected with these twelve labors.

Corona, the Crown, has had many names in its history. It is referred to as the crown Theseus gave Ariadne, the daughter of Minos, King of Crete.

Aquila is referred to in the text in a Korean story. Others tie it in to Ganymede and call it Jupiter who, in the form of an eagle, carried off Ganymede to be cupbearer for the gods.

Cygnus, when the Romans adopted the present name, became associated with the mythical swan identified with Cycnus the son of Mars.

Lyra, the Harp, is said to be the lyre that the mythical musician, Orpheus, played to quell the storm mentioned under Gemini (page 26). Some say Cygnus is Orpheus himself, placed in the sky near his harp.

Perseus is the hero mention on page 18. He is shown carrying the head of Medusa who had writhing snakes for hair. So terrible was she to look upon that a glance would turn the beholder to stone. Perseus carried the bright shield of Minerva and wore the winged slippers of Mercury on his adventure.

Andromeda, the Chained Lady, daughter of Cassiopeia, has been discussed before (page 18).

CONSTELLATIONS ALONG
THE NORTHERN PATH

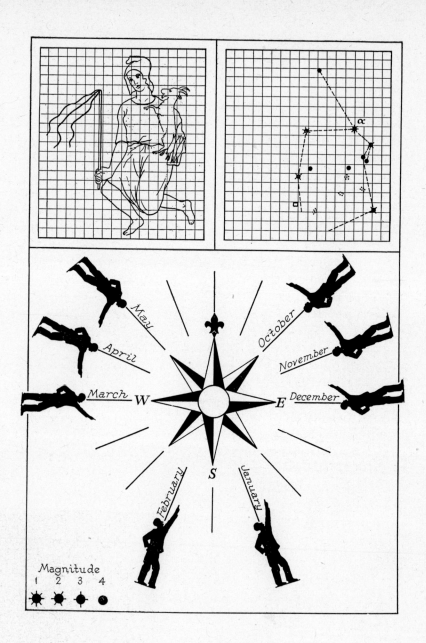

AURIGA — THE CHARIOTEER

★

IN THE old story, Auriga was a goatherd and he is always shown holding a kid in his arms. Capella, α Aurigae, the bright star in this group, means the Goat, and near it is a group of three stars called the Kids. People of many distant countries connected these stars with shepherds, just why we do not know. The stars (if we borrow one from Taurus) are arranged in a pentagon, a five-sided figure. Auriga lies in the midst of the Milky Way.

With the Naked Eye. Note the pale yellow color of Capella. It is 44 light-years away and about 130 times as brilliant as the sun. About 9 o'clock during the middle of January, Capella is almost exactly overhead. Find the three stars that represent the Kids. The star farthest south in the pentagon is El Nath in Taurus, just borrowed for the occasion. This is just off the edge of the chart and is not shown.

With the Opera Glass. All over the area of Auriga you will find many good fields of stars, since the Milky Way is rich here. Look for clusters at the places noted by ∴. Study the color of Capella. It is of magnitude 0.2, that is, nearly a magnitude brighter than first.

With the Telescope. Study more carefully the clusters noted above and look for many doubles within and just around the edges of the pentagon.

OPEN CLUSTER IN AURIGA

This is an "open" cluster of stars. It is called open to distinguish it from a "globular" cluster. The open clusters are much closer to us than the globular type. These clusters are generally moving through space, like a swarm of bees all flying toward the hive. Sometimes the stars are so scattered that it is hard to see them in a telescope. This cluster is known as No. 37 in Messier's catalogue. The photograph was taken at Yerkes Observatory.

★ 55 ★

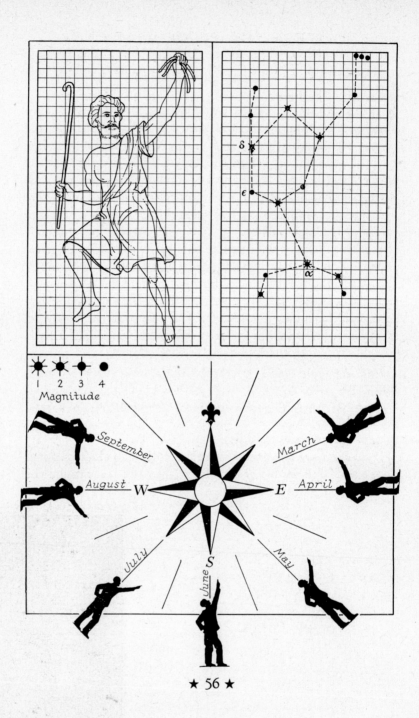

Magnitude

1 2 3 4

September

August   W

July

June   S

May

March

April

★ 56 ★

BOÖTES—THE BEAR DRIVER

★

THIS kite-like figure of five stars is very well-known, and at the end of the kite's tail is the bright star, Arcturus. Boötes is said to be driving the bears around the pole of the sky. Sometimes he is called a ploughman, because the Great Dipper is the plow in some lands.

With the Naked Eye. Arcturus is α Boötis. This brilliant sun is of deep golden or reddish color and, with Vega and Capella, is one of the brightest stars in the sky. Its distance is about 40 light-years and its light opened the Century of Progress in Chicago in 1933. The light was caught in the great telescope at Yerkes Observatory, changed into electricity, sent over telegraph wires to Chicago, and there closed the switch to control the lights. That same light had left the star the year the Columbian Exposition in Chicago had closed (1893). It is a large star, 23,000,000 miles in diameter, 26 times that of the sun, and is 86 times as bright as the sun. This "sun" is moving through space at a rate of 75 miles per second.

With the Opera Glass. Notice the beautiful groups of dim stars near Arcturus. Get Arcturus just outside the field of view.

With the Telescope. ε Boötis is one of the finest doubles; magnitudes 3 and 5; distance 3″; colors, orange and green. This star is 180 light-years away. δ Boötis, magnitudes 3 and 7; distance 2′; colors, yellow and blue.

DOUBLE SPIRAL NEBULA IN BOÖTES

This is a double spiral nebula a twin galaxy of stars. There are twin stars, twin clusters of stars, and twin universes of stars. These dim and distant objects require long exposures, that is, time pictures, not a few minutes, but hours and hours. This one required 6 hours with the 60-inch telescope at Mt. Wilson Observatory. It is designated as No. 5857 in the New General Catalogue.

★ 57 ★

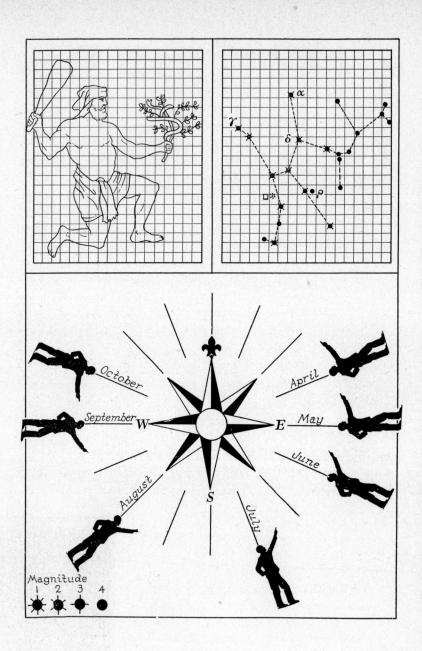

HERCULES—THE STRONG MAN

THIS is a rather large constellation and is best found by a part of it called the Butterfly. The constellation is often known as the Kneeler. The old pictures always show Hercules kneeling with his foot on the head of Draco, the Dragon. There are no very bright stars in this group.

With the Naked Eye. Pick out the wings of the Butterfly and at the place marked ∵ you will see a hazy spot, if the night is dark and clear. This is the great globular star cluster M13.

With the Opera Glass. Study the M13 cluster with the glass and you can see that it is something unusual. This was discovered by Edmund Halley in 1714. The cluster is 34,000 light-years away and contains more than 50,000 stars, perhaps 20 times as many stars as you can ever see in the sky without a telescope.

With the Telescope. Study the M13 cluster and try to see it as a group of stars. α Herculis is double; magnitudes 5 and 5; distance 5''; colors, orange and green. δ Herculis is double; magnitudes 3 and 8; distance 11''; colors, green and white. γ Herculis is double; magnitudes 4 and 8; distance 40''; colors, white and lilac. ρ Herculis is double; magnitudes 4 and 5; distance 4''; colors, shades of green.

GLOBULAR CLUSTER IN HERCULES

The most beautiful globular star cluster in the sky is M13, described above. The distance to these swarms of stars defied the astronomers for many years. But by means of the stars whose light varies—"Cepheid variables," the professionals call them—the distances can now be found. These tiny blinking stars help us span great distances and by light waves alone we can learn a great deal about our universe. The cluster is well known as Messier 13. This picture was taken at Yerkes Observatory.

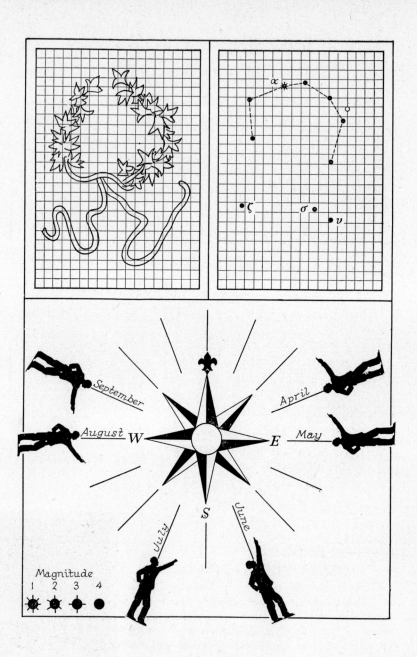

Magnitude
1 2 3 4

September
April
August W E May
S
July June

CORONA BOREALIS—
THE NORTHERN CROWN

THIS circlet of seven stars is one of the most beautiful of all the smaller groups. One jewel in this crown is brighter than the other six. This star is Alphecca, or Gemma Coronae, and is between second and third magnitudes. A nova appeared in Corona in 1866. Some see seven Indian chiefs around the council fire in this constellation. Others call it a horseshoe. This is such a striking little figure that one cannot fail to remember and recognize it.

With the Naked Eye. Perhaps you can see that ν Coronae is a double star. It is yellow. Note the spot O where a nova appeared in 1866.

With the Opera Glass. Study ν Coronae. Note the color. The stars are 10′ apart, and both are fifth magnitude, and yellow.

With the Telescope. ζ Coronae is a double star; magnitudes 4 and 5; distance 6″; colors, white and green. σ Coronae is a double star; magnitudes 5 and 6; distance 5″; one yellow, the other blue.

ECLIPSE OF SUN, JUNE 8, 1937

There are several coronas in the sky: Corona Borealis, the northern crown; Corona Australis, the southern crown; and the corona that appears around the sun at the time of a total eclipse. It is the last that is illustrated here. The corona is a part of the sun's atmosphere and can be seen only when the sun is eclipsed. It changes its shape constantly and at each eclipse appears different. This picture was taken at an elevation of 14,600 feet in the Andes Mountains of Peru by one of the authors. It is one of many pictures taken by the Hayden Planetarium Eclipse Expedition.

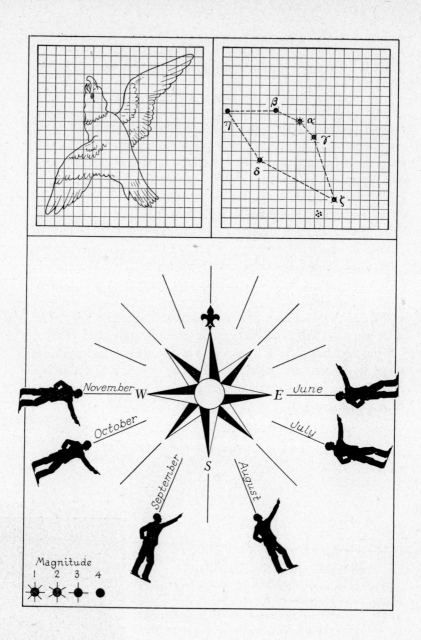

AQUILA—THE EAGLE

ALTAIR, α Aquilae, and a star on either side of it in a straight line are about all of this group that people generally recognize, but it extends into the Milky Way much farther. An old Korean legend says that a shepherd was in love with a girl, and her angry father placed them in the sky, Aquila (the Shepherd) and Lyra (the Girl) with the river (the Milky Way) forever separating them. Their friends, the magpies, each year on the seventh night of the seventh moon form a bridge across the river to unite the lovers.

With the Naked Eye. Find Altair. This is a first magnitude star about 15½ light-years away and shines about 9 times as bright as the sun. Study the variable star η Aquilae. Its brightness changes from 4 to 5 in a period of about 7 days and 4 hours.

With the Opera Glass. Study the variation in η Aquilae. Compare it to other stars in the field, then do it again 3 or 4 days later.

With the Telescope. The cluster near ζ Aquilae is very clear. Notice the fan shape and dark lanes in the cluster.

DARK NEBULA IN AQUILA

In many parts of the Milky Way there are dark spots among the rich star fields. When they were first clearly seen by William Herschel, they were called "holes in the sky." We know now that they are really great clouds of dark gas blotting out the stars that lie beyond, just as sometimes a cloud in our sky blots out the sight of the sun or moon. These spots are called "dark nebulae." This one in the constellation Aquila is a good example of the dark nebulae. In Barnard's catalogue, the nebula is listed as No. 133. The photograph was made at the Mt. Wilson Observatory on July 3, 1921.

★ 63 ★

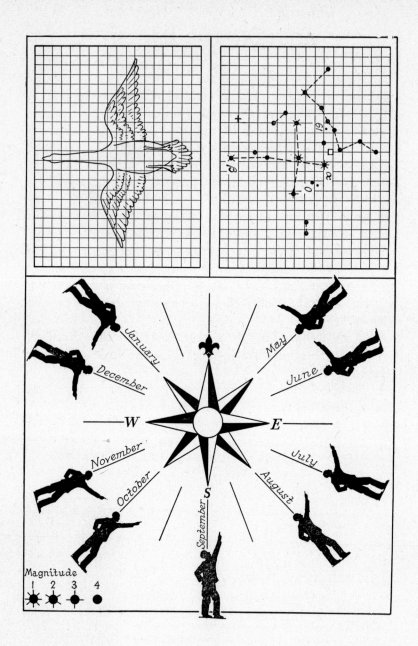

Magnitude
1 2 3 4

CYGNUS—THE SWAN

THIS constellation, in the midst of the Milky Way, contains the Northern Cross. The star at the top of the cross is Deneb, α Cygni. At the foot of the cross is β Cygni, or Albireo. Near Deneb is a dark rift in the Milky Way known as the Northern Coalsack.

With the Naked Eye. Identify Deneb and the Northern Coal Sack. Deneb is more than 650 light-years away and is 10,000 times as bright as the sun. Trace out the Cross and identify Albireo. Find o Cygni. Can you see a small star near this one?

With the Opera Glass. Albireo is one of the finest doubles in the sky and a good field glass will just separate it. It is better studied with the telescope. Find 61 Cygni. It was (page 236) the first star to have its distance measured. It is about 11 light-years away or about 650,000 times as far away as the sun. Study the Coalsack and the rich fields along the Milky Way near Deneb. Examine o Cygni.

With the Telescope. Albireo is a double; magnitudes 3 and 5; 34″ apart; colors, gold and blue. 61 Cygni is also a double; 5 and 6 magnitudes; 23″ apart; colors, gold and blue. o² Cygni, magnitudes 4 and 5; 6′ apart. Locate the Dumbbell nebula, marked ✕, in Vulpecula, a near-by constellation.

NORTH AMERICA NEBULA IN CYGNUS

In this constellation is found the famous North America Nebula. The shape of this beautiful star field explains its name. Here we see thousands of stars and much glowing gas between them—one of the richest and most beautiful regions of the Milky Way. The dark lanes along the "shores" of North America are great clouds of dark gases like a curtain cutting off the sight of the stars that lie beyond. It is designated as N.G.C. 7000. Yerkes Observatory made this fine picture of it.

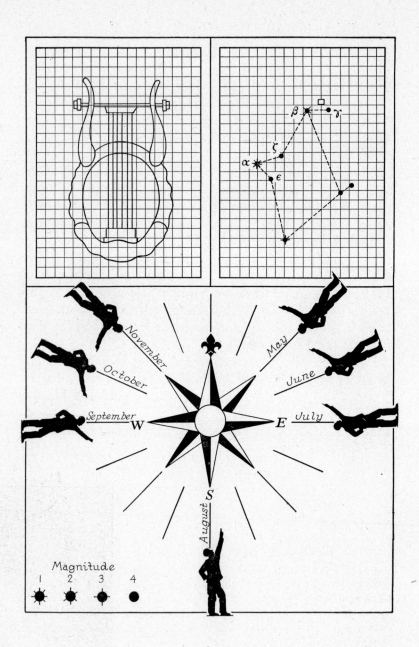

Magnitude
1   2   3   4

LYRA—THE HARP

THIS group is small but has the bright star, Vega, α Lyrae, to make it important. This brilliant white star is second only to Sirius in our sky. It shines in the summer almost overhead. Close by it are two stars forming a little triangle. The northern one of this pair is ε Lyrae. The sun is moving through space at 12 miles per second toward a point near this constellation, called the Apex of the Sun's Way.

With the Naked Eye. Study the triangle of Vega, ε Lyrae, and ζ Lyrae. Observe ε Lyrae carefully and see if you can see it as a double. This is a very rigid test for good eyesight.

With the Opera Glass. ε Lyrae can be easily seen as a double star. Each one is of magnitude 5, and they are 3½′ apart. Study the variable star β Lyrae. It varies from magnitude 3 to 4 in a period of nearly 13 days.

With the Telescope. ε Lyrae is now four stars. Each pair is of magnitudes 5 and 6 and distant 2″ or 3″. O marks the Ring Nebula. You will see it as a hazy smoke ring. ζ Lyrae is a double; magnitudes 4 and 6; distance 44″ apart; colors, yellow and green. β Lyrae is a double as well as variable. It is really four stars forming a Y of 4, 7, 8, and 11 magnitudes—45″, 65″, and 85″ away. You can generally see all four.

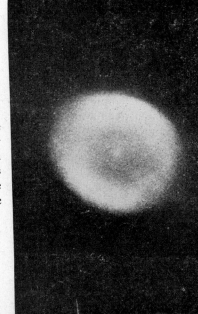

RING NEBULA IN LYRA

Even with a medium-sized telescope you can get a good view of the Ring Nebula in Lyra. It is really a bubble of gas made to glow by the light of the bright star at its center. In a fine photograph like this one made by the 40-inch telescope at Yerkes Observatory on September 9, 1923, you can see much more than you can in any telescope. It is pale green in color and it is so far away that the light requires 800 years to come to us. When did the light that took the picture leave the nebula?

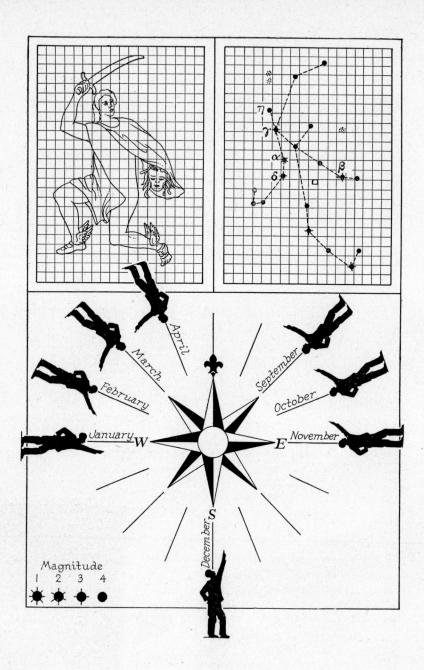

Magnitude

1 2 3 4

PERSEUS—THE HERO

PERSEUS is not an easy group to find in the sky. The constellation is in a rich and beautiful part of the Milky Way. This star group contains the most interesting of the variable stars, the celebrated Algol, or Demon Star as the Arabs called it. So they must have known that there was something peculiar about it. In 1901, a very brilliant and famous nova, or new star, appeared in Perseus. The group is also famous for the "double cluster in Perseus."

With the Naked Eye. Study the variable Algol, β Persei. This is really a double star, one bright and the other dim. The dim one swings around, gets in front of the bright one, and the latter fades out. Generally, Algol is about second magnitude. It stays this bright for 2 days and 11 hours. Then it fades in 5 hours to magnitude 3, and in the next 5 hours brightens to its usual brilliance. Find the double cluster. You can just see it on a dark night. (It is marked ∴ and is above η Persei.)

With the Opera Glass. Observe the double cluster.

With the Telescope. Study the double cluster. It contains hundreds of stars. η Persei is a double; magnitudes 4 and 8; 28″ apart; colors, yellow and blue. Study the other cluster marked ∴. It contains over 100 stars.

EXPLOSION OF A STAR IN PERSEUS

Light travels so swiftly—186,328 miles a second—that generally we think of it as going anywhere instantly. It will go around the earth seven times in a second! But it has been seen traveling! Sometimes a star suddenly flares up and is very bright for a little while. In 1901 such a new star appeared in this constellation. As it was watched night after night, a bright glow appeared around it and the glow grew larger and larger. Why? Well, around the star, before it blew up, was a cloud of dark gas, or fog. The sudden light could be seen traveling out through the gas as these Yerkes pictures show. They were taken on September 20 and November 13, 1901.

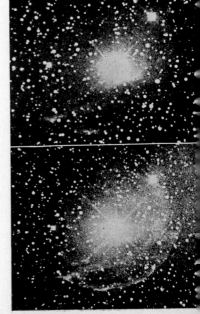

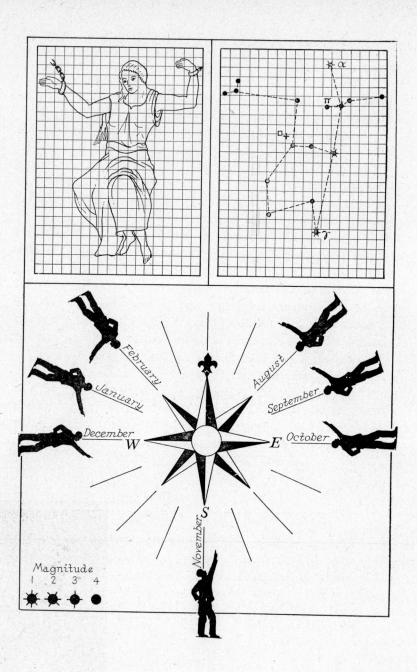

Magnitude
1 2 3 4

ANDROMEDA—THE CHAINED LADY

IT IS marked in the sky by a line of three bright stars nearly equally spaced. The southwestern one is Alpheratz, α Andromedae, the star borrowed to complete the Great Square of Pegasus. The most important object in this group is the Andromeda Nebula, a great galaxy of stars nearly 700,000 light-years away. Yet this is one of the nearest of these island universes. The distance to this great spiral of stars is so great that the following may help us appreciate it. If the distance of the earth to the sun were only 1/10 inch, the nebula would be 70,000 miles away! "Nebula" is not the best word to use for this kind of object. It is not a mass of glowing gas, but is composed of billions of stars. This was proved in 1924 when photographs showed many of them.

With the Naked Eye. If the sky is dark you probably can just see the nebula as a cloudy spot. Look at the place marked +.

With the Opera Glass. α Andromedae (Alpheratz) is second magnitude and nearly 100 light-years away, and is more than 100 times as bright as the sun. Study the Great Nebula.

With the Telescope. γ Andromedae is a fine double star; magnitudes 3 and 5; spaced 10″ apart; colors, orange and blue. It was discovered in 1788 by Mayer. π Andromedae is a double; magnitudes 4 and 8; distance 36″ apart; colors, yellow and blue. Examine the Great Nebula carefully.

NEBULA IN ANDROMEDA

Here we see a small portion at one end of the Great Nebula in Andromeda greatly enlarged. This great whirling universe of stars is so far away that the light takes nearly 700,000 years to come to us. From many studies, it was known to be made up of stars years ago, but no one could see them until 1924. Professor Duncan took this fine picture with the 100-inch telescope at Mt. Wilson Observatory in 1925. You cannot see such fine detail in the telescope.

★ 71 ★

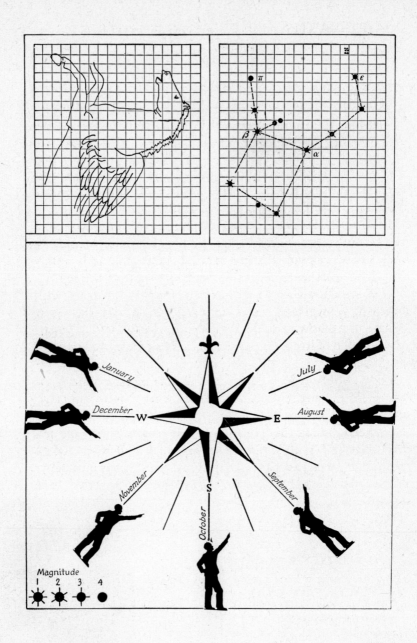

PEGASUS—THE WINGED HORSE

THIS group is better known for the stars that are not there! The Great Square in Pegasus is a large blank space nearly 15 degrees square. There are some very faint stars in it, but you will have to look for them. A person with very good eyesight has counted as many as eighty, but anyone can find fifteen or twenty if the night is dark. One star (at the northeast corner) is borrowed from Andromeda to make the Square. You notice the lines do not quite connect with it.

With the Naked Eye. Count how many stars you can see in the Great Square. π Pegasi is a double star that you may be able to see as two. Identify Markab, α Pegasi. It is nearly 100 light-years away and is 67 times as bright as the sun.

With the Opera Glass. π Pegasi can be easily separated with opera or field glasses into two stars. Sweep over the Great Square to see how many more dim stars you can find. β Pegasi is a variable of irregular period changing from second to third magnitude.

With the Telescope. ε Pegasi is a double star; magnitudes 2 and 8; 2½′ apart; colors, yellow and blue. If you can catch this star on or near the meridian, try this trick of Sir John Herschel's. Swing the telescope a little from side to side, and the little star will appear to swing back and forth like a pendulum or a railroad signal light. Can you guess why? Notice cluster M15, discovered by Miraldi in 1745. It is marked ∴.

CLUSTER IN PEGASUS

This star cluster is known as M15 because Charles Messier numbered it 15 when he prepared his catalogue, listing 103 of these cloudy objects in 1781. Then he did not know how to tell gaseous nebulae from these starry clusters. For 150 years his list has been famous, and today M31 means to every astronomer in the world the Great Andromeda Nebula. M15 means this cluster in Pegasus. Messier intended the list merely for his own use because he was interested in hunting comets and in small telescopes these hazy spots confused him. The list later made him famous.

MYTHOLOGY OF THE CONSTELLATIONS ALONG THE SOUTHERN PATH

CANIS Major and Canis Minor are the two hunting dogs of Orion whose place in mythology is not very clear.

In this same part of the sky you will find *Hydra*, the Water Snake, a monster with nine heads. Hercules tried to kill this creature with his club but for every head he knocked off two grew in its place. Finally he burned off the heads and buried one that was immortal under a rock.

Lepus, the Hare, is close to Orion, the hunter.

Eridanus represents a river. What river is another matter. The Nile, the Po, or even a river of stars—the Milky Way—might be meant.

Cetus, the Whale, is south of Pisces. This is the whale or monster that nearly devoured Andromeda.

These are mentioned on Chart 2, page 83. But along the southern horizon are other unimportant groups—Monoceros, the Unicorn; Puppis, the stern of a ship; Columba, the Dove; Corvus, the Crow; Crater, the Cup; Piscis Austrinus, the Southern Fish.

There are many other star groups that are never above the horizon in latitude 40°. To see them one must go to southern latitudes or at least near the equator. There are many beautiful and interesting constellations in this part of the heavens and those who live or travel there can find many objects to study. Many of these are not among the ancient figures and so have no mythological stories. The early observers lived in the northern latitudes and could not see these stars.

CONSTELLATIONS ALONG
THE SOUTHERN PATH

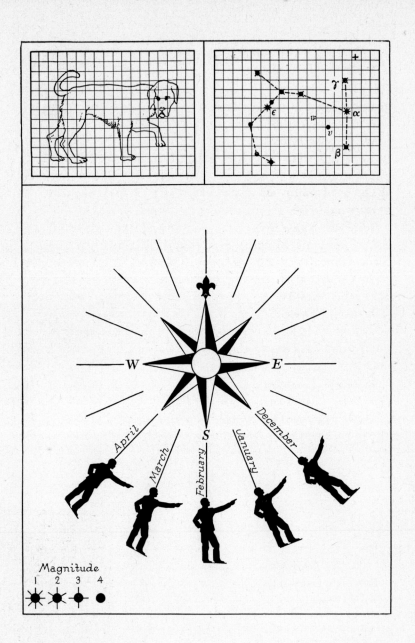

Magnitude
1 2 3 4

CANIS MAJOR—THE GREAT DOG

THIS group is noted because it contains the brightest star in the whole sky. Sirius is commonly known as the Dog Star, perhaps because it served as a watch dog to warn the ancient Egyptians that the Nile River would rise and flood the valley. When they could just see Sirius (Sothis, they called it) coming up in the dawn they knew that soon the river would rise. Its magnitude is about −1.6.

With the Naked Eye. Find Murzim, β Canis Majoris, and Sirius, α Canis Majoris. Note the brilliant white color of Sirius. Since it is always low in our sky, it twinkles more than a star that rises high. It is one of the nearest stars, only 8.6 light-years away, and is 26 times as bright as the sun.

With the Opera Glass. Study the color of Sirius. The Dog Star is a double. If Sirius were not so brilliant you could see its companion in a small telescope. ν Canis Majoris is a triple star and near by is a fine cluster.

With the Telescope. Study ν Canis Majoris more carefully, especially the cluster marked ∴, which is near it. ε Canis Majoris is a double star; magnitudes 2 and 9; distance 7″. See the nebula marked +, northeast of γ Canis Majoris.

A PHOTOGRAPH OF CANIS MAJOR

This photograph shows how this beautiful constellation looks in the large telescope at Yerkes Observatory. The "dark companion" of Sirius, the bright star near the top is so called because it is so small and therefore difficult to see. This tiny sun goes around the Dog Star, just as the earth goes around our sun, but in a period of about 50 years instead of 1 year. The material in this object is far heavier than anything we know of on the earth. It is so dense that a cubic inch would weigh about a ton. A baseball made of such star stuff would weigh about 12 tons. Some baseball!

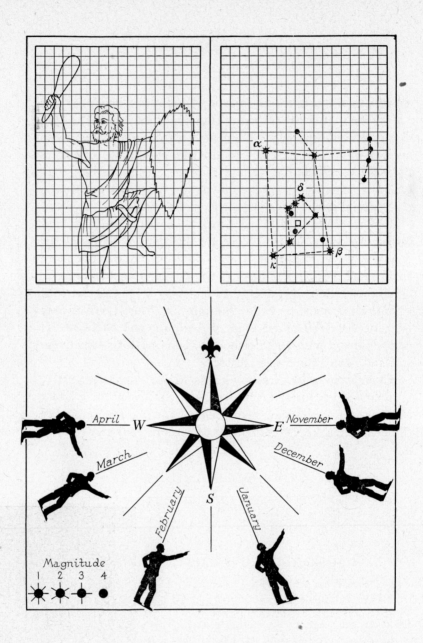

ORION—THE HUNTER

THIS is the brightest and most beautiful of all the constellations that we can see from the United States. The Arabs called this the Central One because it is on the sky's equator.

With the Naked Eye. The three stars forming Orion's Belt make a striking figure. The bright reddish star above is Betelgeuse, α Orionis—the Armpit of the Central One. Below the belt the blue-white star is Rigel, β Orionis.

With the Opera Glass. Notice the beautiful color of Betelgeuse. This star is variable in brightness and now is second to Rigel but is marked α. It is about 400 times as large as the sun and is 272 light-years away. Notice the blue-white color of Rigel. It is 543 light-years away and is 18,000 times as bright as the sun. In the Sword is the Great Nebula in Orion.

With the Telescope. δ Orionis is a double; magnitudes 2 and 7; 53″ apart; white and violet. In the Great Nebula, notice the Trapezium—four stars close together. Near this is a row of three stars which looks like the Belt. Study the beautiful detail in the Great Orion Nebula. Rigel is a double star.

THE GREAT NEBULA IN ORION

The most beautiful nebula in the sky is the Great Nebula in Orion. This great mass of glowing gas is so large that light requires 25 years to go from one side to the other. Light travels over 186,000 miles in a second, so you can work out how large this cloud is. It is so far away from us that 1,800 years are required for light messages to reach us. The gases in the nebula are swirling this way and that with high speed—some up to 8 miles a second. This photograph was taken with the great Yerkes Observatory telescope. In Messier's catalogue the nebula is No. 42.

★ 79 ★

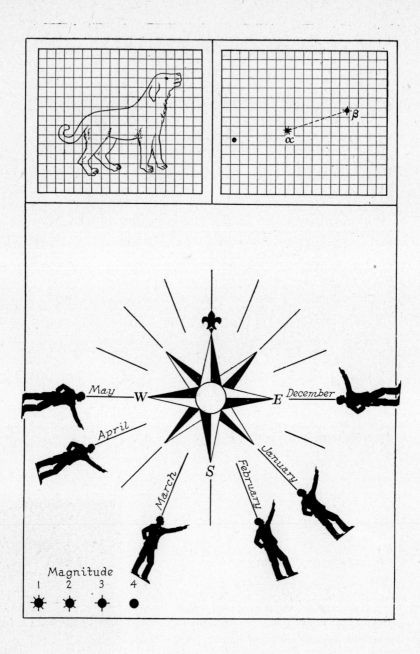

Magnitude
1 2 3 4

CANIS MINOR—THE LITTLE DOG

WE GENERALLY recognize this constellation by one star only. This is Procyon, α Canis Minoris, the Little Dog Star. A Greek word, Procyon means "before the dog," referring to the fact that it precedes the Dog Star, Sirius. These two dogs are generally thought of as the two dogs of Orion, the Hunter.

With the Naked Eye. Procyon is a beautiful yellow star of magnitude 0.5. That is, it is half a magnitude brighter than a first magnitude star. It is about 10.5 light-years away and is 6 times as bright as the sun. Procyon is really a double star, but you can see only one of the pair. The faint star is of thirteenth magnitude and our sun is 17,400 times as bright as this dim star. It is one of the dimmest stars known.

With the Opera Glass. β Canis Minoris, sometimes called Gomelsa, has two stars very near it, one of which is quite red.

With the Telescope. Almost as far southeast of α Canis Minoris as β Canis Minoris is northwest, is a triple star, the components of which are 6, 7, and 8 magnitudes, and are about 1′ and 2′ away.

PELTIER COMET OF 1936

Comets may be first seen in any part of the sky. Not all of them are great fiery objects with luminous tails stretching across the sky. Many comets are discovered each year, but most are so dim that a telescope is needed to see them. Once in a while one is bright enough for the naked eye to see. This picture was taken at Harvard Observatory and shows a comet discovered in the summer of 1936 by a young amateur in Ohio, Leslie Peltier.

STAR CHARTS

Now that you have learned the constellations one by one and become familiar with where and when they may be found, a complete map of the sky will prove interesting and instruc-

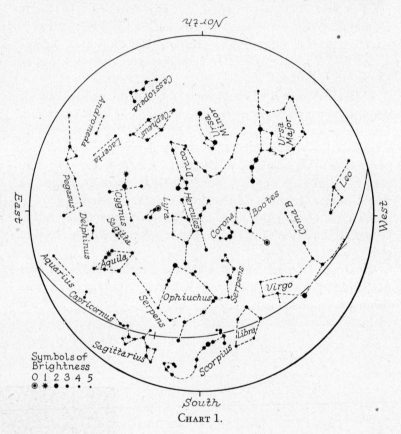

CHART 1.

tive. To portray properly the appearance of the sky and its change from month to month a series of twelve maps should be used. Only two are given here, one representing the winter sky and the other the summer sky. They may be used for other months as well, but not for the same time. Table III will help in using them in the correct way.

★ 82 ★

TABLE III
TIME TABLE FOR USING STAR CHARTS

Chart 1		Chart 2	
January	9 P.M.	April	3 A.M.
February	7 P.M.	May	1 A.M.
March	5 P.M.	June	11 P.M.
October	3 A.M.	July	9 P.M.
November	1 A.M.	August	7 P.M.
December	11 P.M.	September	5 P.M.

These charts are reproduced by permission of the publishers, Whittlesey House, McGraw-Hill Book Company, Inc., from Barton and Barton's *A Guide to the Constellations*.

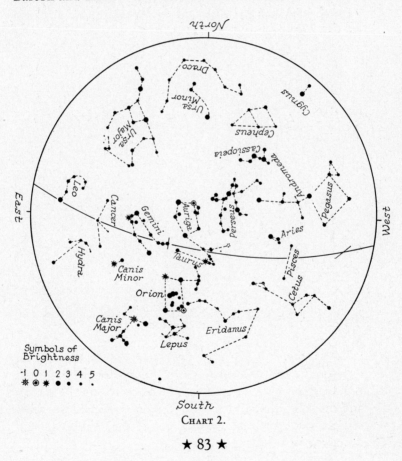

CHART 2.

★ 83 ★

Barton, Samuel G., and William H. Barton: *A Guide to the Constellations*. New York, Whittlesey House, McGraw-Hill Book Company, Inc., 1935.

Bernhard, H. J., Dorothy Bennett, and H. S. Rice: *New Handbook of the Heavens*. New York, Whittlesey House, McGraw-Hill Book Company, Inc., 1941.

Bennett, Dorothy, A: *Star Explorer*. Hayden Planetarium, New York, 1935.

Barton, William H., Jr.: *World Wide Planisphere*. Cambridge, Mass., Addison-Wesley Press, Inc., 1944.

Constellations. Franklin Institute, Philadelphia, 1936.

The Barritt-Serviss Star and Planet Finder. Brooklyn, N. Y., Leon Barritt, 1906.

III

Making Your Own Sky Charts

MANY boys and girls have asked how to make sky charts for their hobby collection. They claim that a book is clumsy and is liable to be damaged during night observations. Yet a diagram or sky chart makes the constellation easier to find, because the eye can pick out the stars which form the figure if there is a model to compare.

Ordinary stiff cardboard is needed for the two kinds of constellation charts described in this chapter. On one type, the stars are represented by gold or aluminum dust paint which shines when a flashlight is pointed at the cardboard. The other kind has holes punched in the cardboard, which look like stars when a flashlight is held behind them. Either type can be easily made. The punched-out chart is more difficult to make, but offers advanced work with a greater amount of astronomical information. It is suggested that you make the simple paint type first. You can go on to the advanced punched-out chart when you have learned the general shape of each constellation.

ACTIVITY A. HOW TO MAKE GOLD DUST (FLASH-ON)
STAR MAPS

Materials. Bronzing liquid or gold paint; light cardboard 6 by 6 inches or larger, or school pencil-tablet cardboard back; a speedball printing pen or a wooden skewer.

Directions.

1. On the cardboard, draw with light dotted lines the general shape of any one constellation as shown on the right-hand side of each page in Chapter II (see Fig. 6).

2. Make small pencil dots on this drawing to represent the different stars.

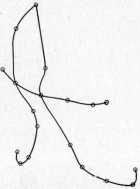

3. Using the speed-ball pen or wooden skewer dipped into the bronzing liquid, make small dots over the pencil dots. Be careful to wait until the paint dries before moving the chart.

4. Using the bronzing liquid, write or print the name of the constellation in the lower right-hand corner of the paper.

5. In small print, label the names of the brighter stars suggested in Chapter II. Make sure that you have the correct name connected to the right star.

FIG. 6.—General shape of a constellation.

Suggestions. With a sharp pin or needle make a small hole through each painted dot. Place the flashlight behind the cardboard.

ADVANCED ACTIVITY B. PUNCHED-OUT (FLASH-THROUGH) STAR MAPS

Materials. Heavy cardboard (obtained from men's laundered shirts), leather punches (sizes, $3/16$ inch, $1/8$ inch, $3/32$ inch, $1/16$ inch), strips of bakelite or flattened strips from heavy tin cans, and a hammer.

Directions.

1. Using a sheet of ruled composition paper, make light pencil cross-section lines on the cardboard (see Fig. 7).

2. Choose one constellation from Chapter II.

3. Count the number of cross-section blocks from any one corner in which each star is located. Make a small circle or dot on your cross-section cardboard, using the correct number of blocks for each star or object.

4. Using the same method (No. 3), outline the mythological figure. Use light pencil lines.

5. Label the magnitude of each star by the correct number. Put this number very near, but not touching the star dots.

Fig. 7.—Making cross-section paper.

Fig. 8.—Punching out stars on charts.

6. Label the names of all bright stars in the same way.

7. Write or print the name of the constellation in the lower right-hand corner.

★ 87 ★

8. Place the bakelite or tin-can strip under the cardboard so that it is beneath the star to be punched out.

9. Hammer the following size punches to make holes for the stars, according to their magnitude (see Fig. 8).

Magnitude.. 1   2   3   4
Punch size, inches................................ $\frac{3}{16}$ $\frac{1}{8}$ $\frac{3}{32}$ $\frac{1}{16}$

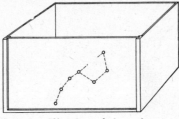

10. If the constellation has a nebula within its outline, cut out a $\frac{3}{16}$-inch hole and cover this with mending tissue.

11. If the constellation has a star cluster within its outline, make a series of pin holes.

12. Print a small letter of the Greek alphabet alongside of the brighter stars named in Chapter II.

FIG. 9.—Illuminated box for star charts.

Suggestions. Secure an ordinary cardboard or wooden box and fix it so that the charts can be changed like slides (see Fig. 9).

ADVANCED READING ACTIVITY

Federer, Charles, and Helen Federer: "Splendors of the Sky," *Sky and Telescope* (monthly), Harvard College Observatory. Cambridge, Mass. [2nd edition, 1943.]

Frost, E. B.: *Let's Look at the Stars.* Boston, Houghton Mifflin Company, 1935.

Martin, John, and C. L. Youmans: *How to Make Sky Pictures.* New York, Greenberg, Publisher, Inc., 1935.

Spitz, Armand: *A Pinpoint Planetarium.* New York, Henry Holt and Company, Inc., 1942.

IV

Meteors

To be outdoors on a beautiful moonlight night is the most enjoyable experience you can have, but really, on a night without a moon, you can have a lot more fun just watching the sky. Then the stars seem brighter and more numerous. An air of mystery and quiet seems to cover the sky, when suddenly our attention is attracted by a "falling star." Quickly one of our friends touches his lips with his thumb, slaps it against his palm, pounds his palm with his closed fist. At the same time he shouts, "Money, money!" "Why are you doing that, Bob?" "That's an old custom, Betty. Our laundress told me that if I did that when I saw a falling star, I would get unexpected money before the next moon."

Of course, we don't believe in old stories like this but it is fun to watch for these falling or shooting stars. Really they are not stars at all! They are not even near the stars. The proper name for these little streaks of light is "meteors." They are very small bits of stone and metal flying through our atmosphere and are not more than 50 or 60 miles above our heads. The stars are millions and millions of miles away from the earth. The old name "falling star" or "shooting star" is still used by many people, but we must not be misled by the incorrect name.

On any clear night, when the moon is not shining, you may see three or four of these meteors in an hour of sky watching.

But if you are familiar with the stars and can point out quickly the important constellations, it is more fun to watch for these fireworks. Then you can tell other boys and girls just where you saw them in the sky. They do look like fireworks. The nice thing about them is that we do not have to wait until the Fourth of July to see them!

All through space are little pieces of matter, like grains of sand, so small that you could hold thousands of them in the palm of your hand. Every once in a while the earth, in its whizzing through space, comes across these wandering mites. The gravity of old Mother Earth stops this wandering and pulls them down toward the ground. They are going through space very fast, perhaps 40 or 50 miles a second. Out in the depths of black space these specks are many times as cold as dry ice. But when they strike the thin air in the stratosphere, 50 or 100 miles above the earth, they suddenly heat up by the friction, just like your hands burn when you slide down a rope. The intense heat lights them up and we see their glowing trail in the sky. In a second or less, they are burned up and disappear. After a little while, perhaps a few minutes, sometimes longer, another meteor flashes. All day long and all night long, we are pelted by these minute shot. And indeed they would be like shot and pierce us if we were not protected by our blanket of air. Aren't we fortunate that we do not live on a body like the moon, where there is no atmosphere to protect the "inhabitants?" Twenty million or more of these space bullets are shot down to the earth every 24 hours! Most of them, fortunately, are small.

Once in a great while, one of these chunks of star dust is so large that it does not burn up so quickly but comes down lower in the stratosphere. Then we see it as an unusually large and bright meteor. This is a fireball or, as astronomers call it, a "bolide." This queer word comes from the same Latin word as ball. Sometimes, a fireball is bright enough to be seen in daylight and frequently we can hear a roaring sound as the ball pushes through the protecting air. Once in a while these startling things burst in the air with a report like a giant rocket, scattering smaller glowing pieces in all directions. This is a real fireworks display!

When a meteor is even larger than this, it may withstand the burning all through the air and strike the ground. The piece may be only as large as a marble, or it may be as big as a baseball, or even larger. These are known as "meteorites" and a few are as massive as boulders. One, which fell in South Africa many years ago, weighs nearly 100 tons and has never

FIG. 10.—Meteor Crater, Arizona. (*Photograph by Clyde Fisher.*)

been moved from the spot where it fell. Thousands of years ago, a still larger one fell in Canyon Diablo in Arizona. It made a wide hole in the ground, nearly a mile across and about 600 feet deep. The picture of this Meteor Crater, as it is called, shows what really happens to Mother Earth when she bumps into a piece of star dust of great size (see Fig. 10). The meteorite shown in Fig. 11 weighs 15½ tons and was found in Oregon in 1902. Many very small pieces sometimes fall at one time. These tiny pieces are like bird shot blasted from a shotgun!

★ 91 ★

Many years ago people viewed meteorites with awe and even refused to touch them or pick them up. They seemed to them like heavenly visitors—too sacred to touch. Others did not believe they actually fell from the sky. Even as late as 100 years ago, Thomas Jefferson, then President of the United States, did not believe there could be such things. He said that he "would rather believe that professors would lie, than stones would fall from the sky." About a century

Fig. 11.—A large meteorite which hit the earth. (*Drawing by Roberta Norton.*)

ago, some experimental scientists were curious to know whether these fiery visitors were made up of the same things as the earth or of unknown materials. Strange to say, it was found that they were made up of the very same materials as Mother Earth. This is a good example of how superstition is overwhelmed by even a little truth. Today no modern person feels anything but interest in these strange inhabitants of space.

On certain nights of the year more than the usual number of meteors may be seen. Your chances of seeing these fireworks on such nights are better than on other nights in the year. They are always more plentiful after midnight than before, because then we are riding around the sun on the front side of the earth—on the front bumper, so to speak. But even earlier on these nights, there are enough to give you a good show, so it is not necessary for you to stay up so late to enjoy watching them.

If you should watch carefully and if you know the constellations, you can make a chart showing the paths of the meteors as you see them against the star figure. If you draw a number of the meteors' paths on those nights when there are "showers," they will appear to come from some particular point in the sky. This imaginary point is called the "radiant." Wherever this center point is among the stars, it takes the particular name of the constellation. For instance, about the middle of November, a radiant seems to be in Leo, the Lion. So this family of meteors are Leonids. Of course these shooting stars do not actually come from Leo, but only appear to do so. Really, they are coming toward us in parallel lines, but just as the parallel railroad tracks seem to meet at a center point away out in the distance, so these parallel meteor trails just look as though they meet. On page 216, there is a special picture that will show this plainly.

One word of warning so that you will not be disappointed. These showers of meteors are generally good on these nights, but you must not accept this list like a program of movies given in the newspapers. A scientist must have patience and accept disappointments without losing interest in repeating the experiment. Scientists understand that it is just as important to know what does *not* happen as what *does* happen.

Table IV gives the dates and places in the sky where the radiant lies. Do not expect the meteor to appear at the radiant. They may first flash at any place in the sky but the trails will seem to go back to the radiant point.

When many watchers from different places observe the same meteor, it is possible to figure out its real path, speed, and other important facts about it. This is a job for a professional astronomer. Such combining is actually done by the American

Meteor Society at the Flower Observatory, University of Pennsylvania, Upper Darby, Pa. If you are interested in joining such a program of meteor watching, you may sign up with the Society for only a dollar a year. Your work will be included with the work of many others, and what to you is merely fun may become of great use in helping to solve the puzzles of the universe. From these studies, we may learn

TABLE IV

METEOR CALENDAR*

Name	Duration in days	Date of maximum number	Hourly no. of all meteors on this date
Quadrantids.................	2	Jan. 2	28
Lyrids.....................	4	April 20	7
Eta Aquarids...............	8	May 2–4	7+
Delta Aquarids.............	3	July 28	27
Perseids...................	35	Aug. 11–12	69
Orionids...................	14	Oct. 19–23	21+
Leonids....................	3	Nov. 14	21
Andromedes................	2	Nov. 24	16
Geminids...................	14	Dec. 11–13	23

* From the table given in *Bulletin* 8, The American Meteor Society.

more about the height and density of the earth's upper atmosphere where some day airplanes may travel at high speeds. Maybe thought must be given to meteors actually hitting the ships of the air and damaging them. From meteors, we may learn something about the origin and development of the solar system, perhaps even facts about the stars way out in space.

SUGGESTED ACTIVITY

If you wish to compare and share your observations with your fellow students, make a record of the facts you observe in the study of meteors. Bring these to your camp, group, or school and post them on the bulletin board where you can compare your observations with those of your friends in a really scientific way. Thus you can form your own meteor society, especially if you save these records. Table V suggests a form to use for your meteor society observations.

TABLE V
RECORD OF METEOR OBSERVATIONS

Date_____Camp or school or group_____Observer_____

Time		Constellation	Color	Seconds visible	Train	Remarks
hr.	min.					
8	27	Leo	White	3	No	Bright

ADVANCED READING ACTIVITY

Nininger, H. H.: *Our Stone-pelted Planet*. Boston, Houghton Mifflin Company, 1933.

Olivier, Charles P.: *Comets*. Baltimore, Williams & Wilkins Company, 1930.

Olivier, Charles P.: *Meteors*. Baltimore, Williams & Wilkins Company, 1925.

Popular Astronomy (monthly). Carleton College, Northfield, Minn.

V

Never Lost with the Stars

How did Christopher Columbus know at night that he was sailing to the west when he started to find a new ocean path to Asia? How did Lindbergh know he was flying to the

Fig. 12.—Ancient navigator finding his position on the ocean.

east toward Paris after the sun had set and stars came out? How do ship captains know where they are on the ocean after they leave sight of land? How did Captain Bligh (about 1789) in the motion picture *Mutiny on the Bounty* know how to steer the frail sailboat 3,000 miles on open seas to reach land?

The answer is written in the motions of the constellations which navigators have to study for sailing purposes. Lindbergh and other aviators, ship captains and explorers must "know their stars" in order to tell exactly where they are on the earth. They must find their latitude and longitude, about which you studied in geography (see Fig. 12).

Many years ago people believed what they saw, and thought the world was flat. Really, it is very reasonable to think so. Look around you and there is not much that would make you think otherwise. If you do not travel over great distances, it makes very little difference if you do believe this. Educated people, however, know that the earth is not flat, but a great big ball—and have known it longer than most

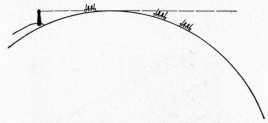

Fig. 13.—Proof that the earth is round.

people suspect. Marco Polo, that great traveler of the thirteenth century, and Christopher Columbus, who crossed the Atlantic Ocean in 1492, knew that the earth was not flat. They understood that the polestar changed its height above the horizon as they journeyed north and south over the globe. Strange as it may seem, Columbus did not think the earth was a sphere but thought it was shaped like a pear.

To those who live inland, it is more difficult to demonstrate that we do live on a round earth. Those who live on the seashore have at hand a very simple proof. When a ship goes out to sea, the tip of the mast or the top of the smokestack is the last part to disappear below the horizon. The ship itself has disappeared long before. This is the usual illustration (see Fig. 13) of the fact that the earth is round. The reverse is also true. When a big luxury liner such as Britain's *Queen Mary* is coming to America, the captain can see the blinking of a lighthouse long before he can see the rock bottom of the lighthouse.

The navigating officer on a ship, or in an airplane, finds his latitude by a method too long for us to study here. We can find our latitude, however, by the simple method that Columbus and Marco Polo used many years ago. They recognized

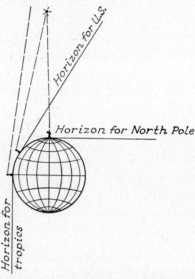

FIG. 14.—Height of the polestar tells the latitude.

the fact that if they were on the equator, the polestar in Ursa Minor, the Little Bear (see page 23), would appear almost on the horizon and if they were at the North Pole, it would stand overhead. At places in between, the North Star would stand above the northern horizon as many degrees as the observer is north of the equator (see Fig. 14). In New York, which is about 41 degrees latitude, Polaris (the polestar) is 41 degrees above the sky line, or a little less than halfway up the sky toward the zenith. The zenith is the point just overhead. This gives the explorer like Byrd, or the navigator like Lindbergh, a way of finding his place on the earth. While this method is not the best, it is so simple that you can easily use it at school or at home, and it is sufficiently accurate for you to check your latitude just as the navigator does.

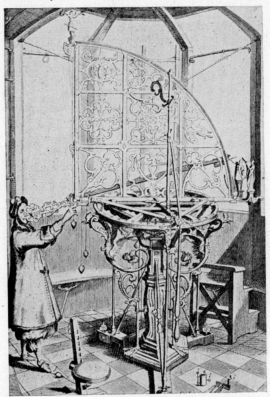

Fig. 15.—Hevelius measuring star positions with a quadrant. (*Yerkes Observatory Photograph.*)

The old navigators and astronomers used a very simple instrument to measure such distances in the sky. It was so crude that the result often was inexact and they lost their way. At night, they might run onto rocks or shoals when they thought they were riding the high seas. This instrument was a cross-staff, which measures angles on a rough scale (see page 103).

★ 99 ★

To improve this simple instrument and to make navigating safer, a new and more accurate device was developed—the astrolabe. This word in Greek means "to take a star." Another useful instrument of the early astronomer is the quadrant. Figure 15 shows Hevelius measuring with this instrument.

FIG. 16.—Modern marine sextant. (*Courtesy Metropolitan Life Insurance Company.*)

Still later came the sextant, sometimes called in old books "the sextant of reflection." It was called a sextant because it was a sixth of a circle or 60 degrees. It is in use today on ships for finding latitude and longitude; Fig. 16 shows a picture of it.

Aviators have developed a newer measuring instrument very much like a sextant, but, since it is the eighth part of a circle, it is called an "octant." The aviator has trouble measuring to the horizon, so this instrument is provided with a bubble—like a carpenter's level. The bubble produces an artificial horizon which is a make-believe horizon. Figure 17 shows a photograph of this instrument.

Would you like to play explorer and find your position on the earth or, as the navigators say, "fix your position"? To do this is really not so difficult as you may think. Of course with your play instrument you cannot do so accurate a job as the ship's officer must do. But you can have the fun of doing it and learning the principle that he uses.

Fig. 17.—Modern aviator's octant. (*Bausch and Lomb Optical Company.*)

First, we must provide ourselves with measuring instruments. If you were wrecked on Robinson Crusoe's island, you could not buy these. You would have to make them.

Perhaps the oldest and certainly the simplest star-measuring instrument is the cross-staff or, as it was sometimes called, "the back staff." The directions given here will help you to build one very much like that used by early navigators— Columbus, for instance. You can see that this does not require much advanced knowledge.

★ 101 ★

ACTIVITY A. HOW TO MAKE A CROSS-STAFF

Materials. Four small wood screws and two iron or brass mending plates, 1 by 5 by ⅛ inches or larger; length of lumber, 40 by 2 by ½ inches; glue; one strip of adding machine paper, 36 inches long.

TABLE VI
CROSS-STAFF DIMENSIONS FOR ANGLES

Angle, degrees	Inches	Angle, degrees	Inches	Angle, degrees	Inches
10	34.3	22	15.5	34	9.8
10½	32.7	22½	16.1	34½	9.7
11	31.2	23	14.8	35	9.5
11½	29.7	23½	14.4	36	9.2
12	28.6	24	14.1	37	9.0
12½	27.3	24½	13.8	38	8.7
13	26.3	25	13.5	39	8.5
13½	25.4	25½	13.3	40	8.2
14	24.4	26	13.0	42	7.8
14½	23.6	26½	12.8	44	7.4
15	22.7	27	12.5	46	7.2
15½	22.1	27½	12.2	48	6.7
16	21.3	28	12.0	50	6.4
16½	20.7	28½	11.8	52	6.1
17	20.1	29	11.6	54	5.9
17½	19.5	29½	11.4	56	5.6
18	19.0	30	11.2	58	5.4
18½	18.4	30½	11.0	60	5.2
19	18.0	31	10.8	65	4.7
19½	17.4	31½	10.6	70	4.3
20	17.0	32	10.5	75	3.9
20½	16.6	32½	10.3	80	3.6
21	16.2	33	10.1	85	3.3
21½	15.8	33½	10.0	90	3.

Directions.

1. Cut lumber into two sections, 36 and 4 inches long.

2. Cut the 4-inch block into halves. Make a 6-inch crosspiece by joining the blocks (2 inches apart) with the mending plates. Cut a small notch at one end (the eye end) of the 36-inch strip.

3. Starting from the eye end, draw cross lines at the designated distances in inches; in the corresponding spaces, write the correct angle, as shown in Table VI.

4. Glue or fasten the white paper strip on the staff.

5. Slip the staff through the crosspiece opening.

6. Press the eye end against your face as shown in drawing (Fig. 18).

Fig. 18.—Observer using cross-staff.

7. Aim at the object to be measured. (For example, Polaris or the North Star.)

8. Slide the crosspiece back and forth until one end just covers Polaris and the other end rests on the horizon.

9. Press the crosspiece in that position and read the angle on the eye side of the crosspiece.

10. Do this several times and "average" the answer. This will give a more accurate answer.

11. This reading will be the angle of Polaris above the horizon.

12. Measure the angle of other objects in the sky.

An instrument very similar to the cross-staff is the quadrant. This is the quarter part of a circle—90 degrees—and is called a quadrant for that reason. With this you can measure altitude in the same way as you did with the cross-staff. It is even easier to use and gives better results. Tycho Brahe used such a quadrant—only a very large one—to make his catalogue of stars.

ACTIVITY B. HOW TO MAKE A QUADRANT

Materials. Thin piece of wood or thick piece of cardboard 8 by 8 inches or larger; a protractor (see teacher); cord or heavy twine attached to lead or iron weight; compass; white paper; two small eyelets; winged nut and bolt (¾ inch) with two flat steel washers; white shellac; a broomstick about 5 feet high, or support as in Fig. 21.

Directions.

1. Use the compass to draw a quarter circle with radius of 6 inches on the wood block.

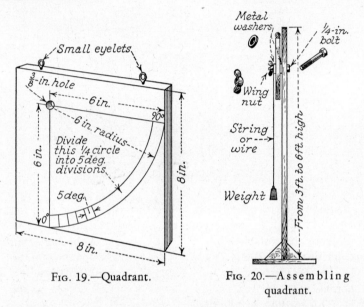

FIG. 19.—Quadrant.

FIG. 20.—Assembling quadrant.

2. With the protractor, divide the quarter circle into 5-degree (5°) divisions. There will be 18 lines going from the center to the circle line.

3. Label each line with the correct angle from 0 to 90 degrees (see Fig. 19).

4. Attaching the eyelets to the 8- by 8-inch board, fasten the quadrant board to the support. Be sure to use the wing nut, bolt, and two metal washers. The board should be loose enough to pivot on the bolt (see Fig. 20).

★ 104 ★

5. Hang the weight in front of the quadrant by tying the string to the bolt.

6. To use the quadrant, look through the two eyelets at the North Star, or Polaris. Swing the quadrant until the star can be seen through both eyelets (see Fig. 21).

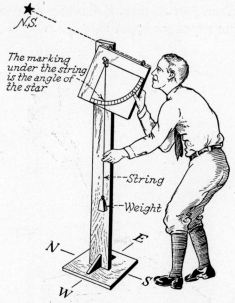

FIG. 21.—Measuring height of polestar with quadrant.

7. Press the string against the board and read the angle under the string.

8. If your quadrant is rigid, the angle of Polaris should be the same as your latitude, north of the equator.

If a quadrant is so mounted that you can swing it around a horizontal circle and read how many degrees you move it from some fixed point, it becomes an altazimuth instrument. This word is made up of parts of two words that now need explanation. Altitude, as you now know, is the angle that an object in the sky stands above the horizon. Azimuth is the angle measured around the horizon from some fixed point of the compass. By general agreement, all astronomers measure azimuth from the south point in the direction, west, north, east, and counting from 0 to 360 degrees. That is, the south point has an azimuth of 0 degrees; the west point, 90 degrees; the north, 180 degrees; while the east point is 270 degrees.

If you wish to keep a record of constellation observations so that you can refer to them in future years, you can mark their location any night by altitude and azimuth. Next year,

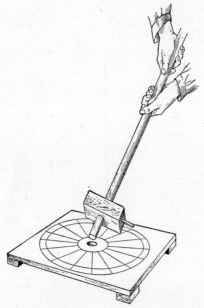

Fig. 22.—Building an altazimuth instrument.

if you repeat this on the same date and at the same time, you will discover the constellation group in that part of the sky having the same altitude and azimuth as your records show! For example, on March 1 at 8 p.m., you measure the altitude and azimuth of Leo, the Lion. You write in your notebook: Azimuth, 315°; Altitude 60°. The next year or any *following* year, if you have not moved from the vicinity, and if you set your altazimuth device to these degrees, your instrument will *again* point to Leo, the Lion.

★ 106 ★

ACTIVITY C. THE ALTAZIMUTH

Materials. Quadrant with broomstick stand, a board, 12 by 12 by ¾ inches or larger; one block, 3½ by 3½ by 1 inch or larger; and one 3-inch finishing nail.

Directions.

1. Draw a circle (5-inch radius) on the board, and divide this in 10-degree divisions. This will make 35 lines.

2. Drill a hole in the exact center of the board. The hole should make a *loose* fit with the broomstick.

3. Drill a center hole in the block (3½ by 3½ inches). This should make a *tight* fit with the broomstick.

4. Drive the nail in the side of this block. This must be in exact line with the quadrant (see Fig. 22).

5. Nail the four 1½-inch blocks on the corners of the board.

6. At the 180-degree line, draw an arrowhead and print N inside of it.

7. At the 0-degree line, draw a tail and print S inside of it.

8. Paint the instrument with white shellac.

9. Set the base stationary with your foot. Turn the bottom block and the quadrant until the nail points to the center of the constellation. Read the azimuth degrees under the nail.

10. In the same position, take the altitude of the constellation. Use the quadrant for this.

11. Record these degrees in your notebook under the name of the constellation, the date, and the exact time. For example:

TABLE VII
ALTAZIMUTH CONSTELLATION RECORD

Date	Time	Constellation	Altitude	Azimuth
March 18	8:45 P.M.	Orion	45°	90°

Modern use of the cross-staff and the altazimuth as instruments of navigation is limited because the altitude angle

Table VIII
SUN DECLINATIONS FOR 1946*
(Corrections for obtaining latitude from sun at noon on any day)

Date	Apparent declination	Date	Apparent declination	Date	Apparent declination	Date	Apparent declination
	° ′		° ′		° ′		° ′
Jan. 1	−23 4	15	−12 57	Apr. 1	+ 4 13	16	+18 54
2	22 59	16	12 36	2	4 36	17	19 8
3	22 54	17	12 16	3	4 59	18	19 21
4	22 48	18	11 55	4	5 22	19	19 35
5	22 42	19	11 33	5	5 45	20	19 48
6	−22 35	20	11 12	6	+ 6 8	21	20 0
7	22 28	21	−10 51	7	6 30	22	+20 13
8	22 21	22	10 29	8	6 53	23	20 25
9	22 13	23	10 7	9	7 16	24	20 36
10	22 4	24	9 45	10	7 38	25	20 47
11	−21 55	25	9 23	11	+ 8 0	26	20 58
12	21 46	26	− 9 1	12	8 22	27	+21 9
13	21 36	27	8 38	13	8 44	28	21 19
14	21 26	28	8 16	14	9 6	29	21 29
15	21 16	Mar. 1	7 53	15	9 28	30	21 38
16	−21 5	2	7 31	16	+ 9 49	31	21 47
17	20 54	3	− 7 8	17	10 10	June 1	+21 56
18	20 42	4	6 45	18	10 32	2	22 4
19	20 30	5	6 22	19	10 53	3	22 12
20	20 17	6	5 58	20	11 13	4	22 20
21	−20 4	7	5 35	21	+11 34	5	22 27
22	19 51	8	− 5 12	22	11 54	6	+22 34
23	19 38	9	4 49	23	12 15	7	22 40
24	19 24	10	4 25	24	12 35	8	22 46
25	19 9	11	4 2	25	12 55	9	22 51
26	−18 54	12	3 38	26	+13 14	10	22 56
27	18 39	13	− 3 14	27	13 34	11	+23 1
28	18 24	14	2 51	28	13 53	12	23 6
29	18 8	15	2 27	29	14 12	13	23 9
30	17 52	16	2 3	30	14 30	14	23 13
31	−17 36	17	1 40	May 1	+14 49	15	23 16
Feb. 1	17 19	18	− 1 16	2	15 7	16	+23 19
2	17 2	19	0 52	3	15 25	17	23 21
3	16 45	20	0 29	4	15 43	18	23 23
4	16 27	21	− 0 5	5	16 0	19	23 24
5	−16 10	22	+ 0 18	6	+16 18	20	23 25
6	15 51	23	0 41	7	16 35	21	+23 26
7	15 33	24	1 5	8	16 51	22	23 26
8	15 14	25	1 29	9	17 8	23	23 26
9	14 55	26	1 52	10	17 24	24	23 25
10	−14 36	27	2 16	11	+17 39	25	23 24
11	14 17	28	+ 2 39	12	17 55	26	+23 23
12	13 57	29	3 3	13	18 10	27	23 21
13	13 37	30	3 26	14	18 25	28	23 19
14	13 17	31	3 49	15	18 40	29	23 16
						30	23 13

* From *The American Ephemeris and Nautical Almanac*, 1946, Government Printing Office, Washington, D. C.

TABLE VIII. (*Continued*)

Date	Apparent declination	Date	Apparent declination	Date	Apparent declination	Date	Apparent declination
	° ′		° ′		° ′		° ′
July 1	+23 10	16	+14 0	Oct. 1	− 2 51	16	−18 32
2	23 6	17	13 41	2	3 15	17	18 47
3	23 2	18	13 22	3	3 38	18	19 1
4	22 57	19	13 3	4	4 1	19	19 16
5	22 52	20	12 43	5	4 24	20	19 30
6	+22 46	21	+12 24	6	− 4 47	21	−19 44
7	22 40	22	12 4	7	5 10	22	19 57
8	22 34	23	11 44	8	5 33	23	20 10
9	22 27	24	11 23	9	5 56	24	20 23
10	22 20	25	11 3	10	6 19	25	20 35
11	+22 13	26	+10 42	11	− 6 42	26	−20 47
12	22 5	27	10 21	12	7 5	27	20 58
13	21 57	28	10 0	13	7 27	28	21 9
14	21 48	29	9 39	14	7 50	29	21 20
15	21 39	30	9 18	15	8 12	30	21 30
16	+21 30	31	+ 8 56	16	− 8 34	Dec. 1	−21 40
17	21 20	Sept. 1	8 35	17	8 56	2	21 50
18	21 10	2	8 13	18	9 18	3	21 59
19	21 0	3	7 51	19	9 40	4	22 7
20	20 49	4	7 29	20	10 2	5	22 16
21	+20 38	5	+ 7 7	21	−10 24	6	−22 23
22	20 27	6	6 45	22	10 45	7	22 31
23	20 15	7	6 23	23	11 6	8	22 38
24	20 3	8	6 0	24	11 28	9	22 44
25	19 50	9	5 38	25	11 48	10	22 50
26	+19 37	10	+ 5 15	26	−12 9	11	−22 56
27	19 24	11	4 52	27	12 30	12	23 1
28	19 11	12	4 30	28	12 50	13	23 5
29	18 57	13	4 7	29	13 10	14	23 10
30	18 43	14	3 44	30	13 30	15	23 13
31	+18 28	15	+ 3 21	31	−13 50	16	−23 17
Aug. 1	18 14	16	2 58	Nov. 1	14 10	17	23 19
2	17 59	17	2 35	2	14 29	18	23 22
3	17 43	18	2 11	3	14 48	19	23 23
4	17 28	19	1 48	4	15 7	20	23 25
5	+17 12	20	+ 1 25	5	−15 25	21	−23 26
6	16 56	21	1 2	6	15 44	22	23 26
7	16 39	22	0 38	7	16 2	23	23 26
8	16 23	23	+ 0 15	8	16 20	24	23 26
9	16 6	24	− 0 8	9	16 37	25	23 25
10	+15 49	25	0 31	10	−16 54	26	−23 23
11	15 31	26	0 54	11	17 11	27	23 21
12	15 13	27	1 18	12	17 28	28	23 19
13	14 55	28	1 41	13	17 44	29	23 16
14	14 37	29	2 5	14	18 0	30	23 13
15	+14 19	30	− 2 28	15	−18 16	31	−23 9
						32	−23 5

obtained is subject to many errors. Inexpensive student model sextants are now available which reduce the amount of angular error to within 30 seconds of arc. You might be on the lookout for used professional sextants and octants which are sometimes offered for sale. These commercial devices, of course, reduce the angular error to a very small figure.

The next activity, that of obtaining your latitude by the meridian altitude of the sun, is being offered for use on the primitive instruments you have made. The sun reaches its highest point on the north and south meridian at solar noon (see Chapter VIII). By doing this activity, you can learn the fundamental operations involved and thus will be much better prepared to advance in the use of more precise instruments and systems of navigation.

The point to remember in using this method is that you must subtract the sun's meridian angle from 90 degrees (90°). On March 21, the vernal equinox, and on September 21, the autumnal equinox, this result will be your latitude. On all other days of the year there is another simple arithmetical step to perform. On some of these days you must *add* a correction figure to obtain the latitude, and on other days you must *subtract* a correction figure. These correction figures are found in Table VIII, on pages 108 and 109. There are several other corrections that enable a professional navigator to calculate his position even more exactly. These are beyond the scope of this book, and you are advised to consult the references at the end of the chapter for more advanced study.

ADVANCED ACTIVITY D. SHOOTING THE SUN

Materials. Cross-staff or altazimuth or sextant; dark glasses to protect your eyes from the bright sun; watch.

Directions.

1. About 15 minutes before Solar (see page 152) noon, measure the altitude of the lower rim of the sun above the horizon; record this angle.

2. Repeat this measurement every five minutes until 15 minutes after solar noon.

★ 110 ★

3. Average your record of altitude angles; subtract from 90°.

4. Refer to the table* of sun declinations on pages 108 and 109. Run down the columns until you find the correct date of the month; note whether there is an addition or subtraction symbol in front of it.

5. Add or subtract this correction figure to your averaged altitude angle.

6. The answer is your latitude.

Examples.

1. On March 21, 1945, the averaged meridian altitude of the sun was 50°. Subtracting this from 90°, gives 40° as the latitude.

2. On December 21, 1945, the averaged meridian altitude of the sun was 26°30′; subtracting from 90°, gives 63°30′. Next, running down the column to December 21 in Table VIII, pages 108 and 109, the correction figure of −23°26′ is found. Subtracting this from 63°30′ gives an answer of approximately 40° latitude.

Within the past few years research scientists working under pressure of the needs of a global war have written and devised many new methods of celestial navigation. All of these tried to simplify the standard ways of determining the ship's or plane's position and course. This simplification was done to save time and to enable more young people to qualify as pilots and navigators. In order to work out the precise calculations of any of these procedures, however, it is necessary to use numerous technical instruments and devices.

One of the authors† of this book felt the need of a system of navigation which could be used for emergency purposes on the high seas, deserts, or remote land points, even when no technical instruments other than a watch were available. The needed charts, he also believed, might be reduced to a few

* This table is for the year 1946. It can also be used for a few years prior to and after this date. Your answers in other years will not vary much from the precise answer needed for seamanship, taking into consideration the limits of accuracy of the instruments used.

† A few months previous to his death, Professor William H. Barton, Jr., completed a unique and simple method of approximating position, course, and distance, which he called "Thumb Nail Navigation," in a pamphlet published in December, 1943. In this pamphlet he states that "the method grew out of a statement on an allied subject made by one of my former navigation students, Lieutenant (j.g.) Robert G. Spencer, U.S.N.R." It is this method which is being presented in this edition with special permission of Addison-Wesley Press, Inc., publishers of "Thumb Nail Navigation."

which could be folded into a waterproof section of a wallet or pocketbook. This method requires less time to work than to describe. An observer would indeed never be lost with the stars once he has acquired the techniques of this concise or "thumbnail" system.

The areas of the world covered by the charts* given here are for the east and west coasts of the Northern Hemisphere from the equator to about 60°N. Lat., for the west coast of Europe and Africa from the equator to 60°N. Lat., and for the east coast of Asia covering the same latitudes.

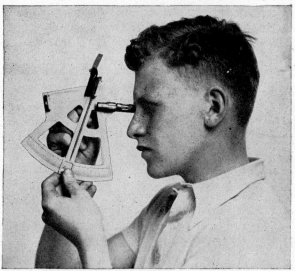

FIG. 23.—Student using sextant. (*Courtesy Boyce-Meier Equipment Company.*)

To learn "thumbnail" navigation, you must know

1. Enough about the sky to recognize a point among the stars and to find it on the star chart with certainty. That is, a sky point may be midway between two stars you recognize on the chart, or in line with them, or making a triangle or other simple figure. Unless you learn to do this, you cannot

* Acknowledgment is made to Admiral G. S. Bryan, Hydrographer, for permission to adapt charts H.O. 2100, and H.O. 1262A.

use this method of thumbnail navigation or any other method depending upon the stars. You need not know many star or constellation names, but it will help a great deal to know them so that you can more readily use the star charts (see Chapter II).

2. How to convert your watch time to G.C.T., unless you keep this time on your watch. You must also know how fast or slow your watch is.

3. How to find the zenith (the point overhead) on the sky. Some observers can locate this point by eye, but sighting up along a plumb line is a help. Hold the end of the line overhead, shut one eye, and move the string until you can look up along it, or along the middle of its swing. Note the point in the sky marked by the end of the string and locate it on the star chart. Lying on your back will make the sighting easier. Check your observation several times (see Fig. 24).

4. Enough about seamanship to sail on a given course. The nearest shore is not necessarily the best one to try to make. Contrary winds or

FIG. 24.—Observer finding zenith.

currents may make a longer route desirable. The pilot chart plus your own knowledge and experience are the best guides on this subject. This method provides only the navigation.

5. How to read a world star chart (right ascension and declination). You will recall that latitude and longitude to a geographer mean the location of a place on the earth north or south of the equator and east or west of Greenwich, respectively. A similar system of locating sky objects is used in astronomy, except that these circles are named right ascension (R.A.) and declination (Dec.). Up to this time,

your location of sky objects has been limited to altitude and azimuth angles.

In geography, the zero point for longitude is Greenwich; in astronomy, the zero point for R.A. is the vernal equinox in the constellation of Pisces, the Fishes (see page 45). Going from this point west to east among the constellations, R.A. is measured in hours, minutes, and seconds from 0^h to 24^h. On the World Star Chart these numbers are found at the top and bottom of the page. There are also five faint lines between each hour which are convenient in approximating 10-minute intervals. It is, of course, impossible to note the second differences on this type of chart.

Again, in geography, the zero point for determining north or south latitude is the terrestrial equator; in astronomy, this is the celestial equator or equinoctial found in the center of the chart. Instead of latitude, the name declination (Dec.) is used, with points on this equator being 0 degrees (0°). North declination includes all objects north of the equinoctial and is labeled plus (+), for example, +20° Dec. South declination means all objects south of the equinoctial and is labeled minus (−), for example, −20° Dec. Declination runs from 0° to +90° to −90°. These numbers are found on the right and left edges of the chart. There are four faint lines between each 10-degree Dec. which are aids to approximating 2-degree intervals in the sky.

Example.

β Persei (see page 69) can be given an approximate sky location of R.A. $3^h 2^m$ and declination of +41°.

ADVANCED ACTIVITY E.   THUMBNAIL NAVIGATION

Materials. Right Ascension (R.A.) and Declination (Dec.) star chart, facing page 114; sectional maps of the world, facing page 112; a watch running Greenwich Civil Time (G.C.T.); plumb line and bob (may be a piece of string and a small weight such as a nut or bolt); a copy of the navigation record on page 118; a copy of month correction table on page 117.

Directions.

1. Locate the point overhead by estimate or by using the plumb line and mark this point among the stars *Z* on the star chart. If you are in the zone for which your watch is set, or can get your zone time, add to the hours since noon the number opposite the date in the table on page 117. Your zenith will be near the R.A. represented by this sum and near the declination that approximates your latitude. It will help to get this approximate point first. Find it in the sky and then make the more careful determination of your zenith.

2. Read along the scale at the top of the star chart the hours of R.A. (to the nearest quarter hour) of the point you marked *Z*, and along the side scale find the degrees of its declination. Record the values in lines 6 and 8 in the blank table on page 118. After some practice the entire problem can be worked mentally.

3. Set down the hours since noon (better make the reading at a full hour, half, or quarter) to the nearest quarter-hour, in line 1 or line 3. That is, 10:25 P.M. is $10\frac{1}{2}$ hours since noon and 3:40 A.M. is $15\frac{3}{4}$ hours. Find the Greenwich hours since noon in line 3.

4. Add the month correction from the table on page 117 to get the R.A. of Greenwich—lines 4 and 5. If the result of this addition is over 24, subtract 24 and use the remainder only. Mark this R.A. hour along the top of the star chart *G*. You can mark this to the nearest quarter-hour of R.A.

5. Subtract line 6 from line 5 (or line 5 from 6) to get your longitude east or west of Greenwich. Note whether *Z* is east or west of *G*. This gives you line 7. From that and line 8 plot your position on the proper map. Your zenith bears the same relation to the Greenwich zenith as your position bears to Greenwich itself. With practice this can be done without writing any of the figures.

6. The next step is to select a destination. Mark it *D* on the chart and record its latitude and longitude on the blank on page 118. Lay off this same longitude (now called R.A.) east or west of the point you marked *G* on the star chart. If you run off the edge, continue from the other edge. Twenty-four hours is the same as 0 hours. This will locate the meridian in the sky over your destination. Lay off along this meridian the latitude of your destination. Mark this point *D*. That spot in the sky was exactly over the destination at the watch time recorded. Note its place among the stars on the chart. Look into the sky and find this spot. That is your heading. If you

have consumed a quarter- or half-hour working the problem, move *D eastward* on the star chart a corresponding amount, keeping the same declination. That is your present heading.

7. You can check and correct your heading every 2 or 4 hours by moving the point *D* along the same declination 2 or 4 hours *eastward*. These points may be marked with the time *D*8, *D*10, etc., and may be used on succeeding nights 4 minutes earlier than the time for the preceding night. Thus, if you worked the problem at 8 P.M. on July 20, the same spot in the sky will be over the destination at 7:56 on July 21 and at 7:52 on July 22. Reworking the problem on succeeding nights, however, will check the work. As you approach the destination, *Z* and *D* will approach each other, and finally coincide.

8. The above fact is the basis of measuring the distance to the destination by the stars. The angle in degrees on the sky between your zenith and the destination zenith multiplied by 60 is the number of nautical miles between you and the destination. To measure sky distances in degrees, note on the chart the distance in degrees of declination between two known stars that are in a north-south line. The pointers in the Dipper, for example, are $5\frac{1}{2}$ degrees apart; the eastern or western edge of the Great Square in Pegasus is about 14 degrees long. Holding your hand at arm's length, measure one of the "yardsticks" with your fingers and see how many times this length goes into the distance from your zenith to the destination zenith.

Example.

From a lifeboat somewhere in the North Atlantic Ocean, an observer sights his zenith as a point along the eastern edge of the Great Square in Pegasus, as far north of Alpheratz as Algenib is south of it. The date is August 15 and his watch, keeping Eastern Standard Time (+5 Zone), reads 1:14 A.M., but is 6 minutes slow.

Position. The correct time is 1:14 plus 06, or 1:20, $13\frac{1}{4}$ hours since noon (line 1). Add 5 hours (line 2) to get Greenwich hours since noon (line 3). Month correction from the table for August 15 is $9\frac{1}{2}$ (line 4). Sum (line 5) is $27\frac{3}{4}$. Subtract 24, leaving $3\frac{3}{4}$. Mark *G* at the $3\frac{3}{4}$ hour of R.A. on the star chart. Mark the observer's zenith *Z* on the star chart. At the top read 0 hours R.A.; at the side, 44 degrees N. declination. Put these values in lines 6 and 8. Subtract line 6 from 5 and insert $3\frac{3}{4}$ in line 7, striking out *E*. Mark *Z* on the North Atlantic chart at $3\frac{3}{4}$ hours west longitude, 44 degrees north latitude—off the Nova Scotia coast.

Destination and course. For reasons known to the navigator only, he selects the tip of Florida as his destination and marks it D on the chart. Its latitude and longitude are read as 25 degrees north and $5\frac{1}{2}$ hours west of Greenwich. Counting along the scale on the star chart $5\frac{1}{2}$ hours west of G (running off the right-hand edge and continuing from the left-hand edge) gives $22\frac{1}{4}$. Mark it D. Run down to 25 degrees; mark that D also. It is in line with η and Enif,

TABLE IX

MONTH CORRECTION TABLE

Date	Add	Date	Add	Date	Add	Date	Add
Jan. 1– 4	$18\frac{3}{4}$	Apr. 2– 5	$00\frac{3}{4}$	July 3– 5	$6\frac{3}{4}$	Oct. 2– 5	$12\frac{3}{4}$
5– 8	19	6– 9	1	6– 9	7	6– 9	13
9–11	$19\frac{1}{4}$	10–13	$1\frac{1}{4}$	10–13	$7\frac{1}{4}$	10–12	$13\frac{1}{4}$
12–15	$19\frac{1}{2}$	14–17	$1\frac{1}{2}$	14–17	$7\frac{1}{2}$	13–16	$13\frac{1}{2}$
16–19	$19\frac{3}{4}$	18–20	$1\frac{3}{4}$	18–21	$7\frac{3}{4}$	17–20	$13\frac{3}{4}$
20–23	20	21–24	2	22–25	8	21–24	14
24–27	$20\frac{1}{4}$	25–28	$2\frac{1}{4}$	26–28	$8\frac{1}{4}$	25–28	$14\frac{1}{4}$
28–31	$20\frac{1}{2}$	29– 2	$2\frac{1}{2}$	29– 1	$8\frac{1}{2}$	29–31	$14\frac{1}{2}$
Feb. 1– 3	$20\frac{3}{4}$	May 3– 6	$2\frac{3}{4}$	Aug. 2– 5	$8\frac{3}{4}$	Nov. 1– 4	$14\frac{3}{4}$
4– 7	21	7–10	3	6– 9	9	5– 8	15
8–11	$21\frac{1}{4}$	11–13	$3\frac{1}{4}$	10–12	$9\frac{1}{4}$	9–12	$15\frac{1}{4}$
12–15	$21\frac{1}{2}$	14–17	$3\frac{1}{2}$	13–16	$9\frac{1}{2}$	13–16	$15\frac{1}{2}$
16–18	$21\frac{3}{4}$	18–21	$3\frac{3}{4}$	17–20	$9\frac{3}{4}$	17–19	$15\frac{3}{4}$
19–22	22	22–25	4	21–24	10	20–23	16
23–26	$22\frac{1}{4}$	26–29	$4\frac{1}{4}$	25–28	$10\frac{1}{4}$	24–27	$16\frac{1}{4}$
27– 2	$22\frac{1}{2}$	30– 1	$4\frac{1}{2}$	29–31	$10\frac{1}{2}$	28– 1	$16\frac{1}{2}$
Mar. 3– 6	$22\frac{3}{4}$	June 2– 5	$4\frac{3}{4}$	Sept. 1– 4	$10\frac{3}{4}$	Dec. 2– 5	$16\frac{3}{4}$
7– 9	23	6– 9	5	5– 8	11	6– 8	17
10–13	$23\frac{1}{4}$	10–13	$5\frac{1}{4}$	9–12	$11\frac{1}{4}$	9–12	$17\frac{1}{4}$
14–17	$23\frac{1}{2}$	14–16	$5\frac{1}{2}$	13–16	$11\frac{1}{2}$	13–16	$17\frac{1}{2}$
18–21	$23\frac{3}{4}$	17–20	$5\frac{3}{4}$	17–20	$11\frac{3}{4}$	17–20	$17\frac{3}{4}$
22–25	00	21–24	6	21–23	12	21–24	18
26–29	$00\frac{1}{4}$	25–28	$6\frac{1}{4}$	24–27	$12\frac{1}{4}$	25–27	$18\frac{1}{4}$
30– 1	$00\frac{1}{2}$	29– 2	$6\frac{1}{2}$	28– 1	$12\frac{1}{2}$	28–31	$18\frac{1}{2}$

one third the way from η. He has consumed a half-hour on the problem, the watch reading 1:44. Therefore move D a half-hour eastward, at the little unmarked star near the western edge of the Great Square. Take a heading on it. In an hour D will be nearly in the center of the Great Square. Correct your heading to that point.

TABLE X
HOW TO DETERMINE POSITION

Line	Your Position	Example	
1	Hours since noon	13¼	
2	Zone (add W, sub E)	5	
3	Grnch. Hr. since noon	18¼	
4	Month corr. (add)	9½	
5	R.A. Greenwich "G"	27¾	
6	R.A. your position Z	0	
7	Your Longitude (E)(W)	3¾ W	
8	Your Latitude (N)(S)	44 N	

TABLE XI
HOW TO DETERMINE DESTINATION

Destination	Example	
Latitude (N)(S)	25 N	
Longitude (E)(W)	5½ W	

ADVANCED READING ACTIVITY

Aircraft Navigation Manual. U. S. Hydrographic Office, Publication 216, Washington, D. C.

Alter, Dinsmore: *Introduction to Practical Astronomy.* New York, The Thomas Y. Crowell Company, 1933.

American Air Almanac (quarterly). U. S. Naval Observatory, Washington, D. C.

American Nautical Almanac. (annual). U. S. Naval Observatory, Washington, D. C.

Barton, William H., Jr.: *An Introduction to Navigation.* Cambridge, Mass., Addison-Wesley Press, 1944.

Barton, William H., Jr.: *Stereopix for Celestial Navigation.* Cambridge, Mass., Addison-Wesley Press, Inc., 1943.

Bowditch, Nathaniel: *American Practical Navigator.* U. S. Hydrographic Office, Publication 9, Washington, D. C., 1938.

Dead Reckoning Altitude and Azimuth Tables (Ageton's Method). U. S. Hydrographic Office, Publication 211, Washington, D. C.

Dutton, Benjamin: *Navigational and Nautical Astronomy.* U. S. Naval Institute, Annapolis, Md., 1942.

Jacoby, Harold: *Navigation.* New York, The Macmillan Company, 1918.

Mixter, George W.: *Primer of Navigation.* New York, D. Van Nostrand Company, 1941.

Navigation Tables for Mariners and Aviators (Dreisonstok's Method). U. S. Hydrographic Office, Publication 208, Washington, D. C.

Vosseller, Perry: *Navigation.* New York, Rudder Publishing Company, 1938.

Weems, Philip, V. H.: *Air Navigation.* New York, McGraw-Hill Book Company, Inc., 1938.

Wylie, Paul: *The Essentials of Modern Navigation.* New York, Harper & Brothers, 1942.

VI

Where Is the World Going?

A. THE SOLAR SYSTEM

SPACE ships traveling from planet to planet have been prominent on the radio and in newspapers. These stories have
thrilled the imagination of people who enjoy thinking about
the dizzy speeds and strange possibilities of man journeying
out into space. Modern astronomy has discovered that this
round earth itself is a space ship, whizzing through about
400,000,000 miles a year in a big spiral in the sky. Besides,
it is spinning 1,000 miles per hour on its axis and rolling 18½
miles per second around the sun. Perhaps you learned about
this in geography. It requires some explanation and is a new
idea compared to what was originally believed about where
the earth was going.

The average man of ancient times never bothered about
wondering just where the world was going, because to his
way of thinking the earth was stationary. The sun, the stars,
the moon, and the planets moved in the sky but the earth was
fixed. Everyone said you could not feel it move! This was
known as the geocentric theory, from *geus*, the "earth,"
and *centric*, the "center"; that is, everything in the sky
circled about the stationary earth. The Chinese believed the
earth to be supported on seven stone pillars. The Hindus
thought that the earth was resting on the back of an elephant

who stood on the back of a turtle! The Greeks pictured the earth being carried upon the shoulders of Atlas, their strong-man god. All these forgot to mention, however, what was supporting their supporter!

Learned men, especially astronomers and philosophers, suspected that these tales were false. Most of these men agreed that the earth was a sphere, but they disagreed upon the idea of motion. Did the sun circle the earth, or did the earth circle the sun? Finally, during the middle of the second cen-

Fig. 25.—Ptolemy believed the earth to be the center of the universe. (*From a page of a book printed in* 1658. *Courtesy Yerkes Observatory.*)

tury after Christ (about A.D. 135 to 160) the matter was suppos-edly settled. One of the most famous astronomers, Ptolemy, who was an authority of his time, announced that the earth was a ball which did not move from its spot in space, and that the sun and moon were planets which revolved about the world with the other five planets (Mercury, Venus, Mars, Jupiter, and Saturn). He explained that the fixed stars also circled about the earth, but much more slowly (see Fig. 25). This geocentric idea was called the "Ptolemaic theory." For nearly 1,400 years this theory was the answer to the little

★ 121 ★

questioning that was done about where the earth was going. But the people refused to believe that the earth was round because they said that you could see it was flat! It must be remembered that Ptolemy came to these conclusions through logic.

Many astronomers believed this idea was false, but none dared openly to deny it, because it was dangerous to argue against an authority who said it was so! The "sun circling the earth" remained as the truth until after Columbus discovered America. Then a Polish monk, named Copernicus, who liked to think about the stars and who had studied them for many years in a quiet monastery, found errors in Ptolemy's idea. He believed this notion to be wrong and in 1543 published his famous book *De revolutionibus orbium coelestium*, in which he stated that the earth was a planet, or "moving star," like Mercury, Venus, Mars, Jupiter, and Saturn, and also that these planets circled around the fixed sun. In simple words, Copernicus said, "The earth is not the center of the universe, but the sun is." This indeed was a revolution which broke the thinking tradition of 1,400 years. Copernicus' idea was known as the "heliocentric theory," from *helio*, the "sun," and *centric*, "to circle about," the word meaning, therefore, to circle about the sun (see Fig. 26). Because he realized that he would be burned at the stake if he opposed the authorities, Copernicus delayed publishing his theory until he was dying of old age. Like Ptolemy, Copernicus used logic and had no facts to prove that his theory was right and that the great Ptolemy was wrong.

When Copernicus' book was announced, it inspired the scientific search for facts to see if his theory was correct. It also prompted the building of many models to show how the planets did revolve about the sun as he said they did. Tycho Brahe, the Danish astronomer (about 1600), measured the motion of the planets and the stars for many years, and kept an accurate record of these observations. In the meantime, Galileo, the Italian astronomer (about 1610), squinting through his homemade telescope, was amazed when he saw four tiny moons circle around the planet Jupiter, on regular roads as it were (see Fig. 55). Here was the first step in proving that Copernicus' crazy idea *might* be scientifically correct. Galileo nearly lost his life for believing this. It remained for Tycho Brahe's pupil, Johannes Kepler, a German astronomer, (about 1650), to *prove* by drawings and mathematics that

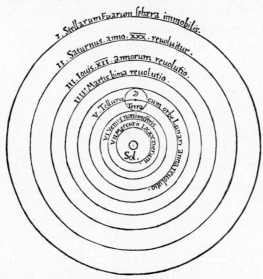

Fig. 26.—Copernicus believed the sun to be the center of the universe. (*An illustration in his "De revolutionibus," 1566. Courtesy Yerkes Observatory.*)

Ptolemy was wrong and Copernicus was right. Kepler predicted the positions of all the planets as they went around the sun in flattened circles, called "ellipses." Kepler put his answer into "laws" which proved that Copernicus was almost entirely right; the earth was a planet, and all the planets did revolve about the sun in ellipses. Sir Isaac Newton, an Englishman who has been called the greatest astronomer, put the final touches on proving that Copernicus was correct. This was the beginning of the end for Ptolemy's geocentric theory. Newton took up where Kepler's mind did not go. Kepler had shown *how* the planets actually did move in a sort of a merry-go-round with the sun fixed almost in the center of them. Newton worked out *why* the sun kept the world and the other planets forever rolling around their elliptic paths, without flying off into space. Thus, in about 200 years (1536–1732) man could answer with more science and less guessing, just where the earth was going.

It seemed that Newton had settled this question once and for all when, in 1783, Sir William Herschel, the English astronomer, announced that our supposedly "fixed" sun was moving toward that part of the sky where the constellation Hercules is located (see page 59). This strengthened man's changing idea that the earth was not the center of the universe. Now, the solar system became a small part of something larger. Curiosity was again aroused in the minds of thinking people. If the sun were moving, and the earth and the planets circled the sun in elliptic orbits, then where was humanity on the earth going? This is the question which modern astronomy is trying to answer. Since Hercules is a faint, difficult-to-find constellation, the place toward which the world is going is better explained by saying that it is not far from Vega, the brightest star in Lyra, which is not far from Hercules (see page 66).

If your imagination is good, picture the earth rotating on its axis, spinning about the sun and at the same time moving in a spiral through space toward Vega. It is moving just like the radio and the newspaper space ships. Can you imagine the earth being 400,000,000 miles farther out in space for every year of its existence? Why can't we see just what is ahead of us in space? Tonight, or any clear night from May to November, look at the mysterious spot near Vega; and gaze toward the end of the world's journey! Do this as you leave the movies or come back from milking the cows or are busy with the various things that boys and girls from Portland, Me., to Portland, Ore., are always doing. Pause for a moment from your life's activities and think—at this very second— that, as you are reading this, everyone on the earth is going

12 miles per second toward this point in the heavens near Vega!

Most people can form a clearer picture in their minds if they can see a drawing or, better, a model. The following are directions for making models which should illustrate to you what the earth and the solar system would look like if you had a grandstand seat away out in space.

ACTIVITY A. HOW TO MAKE A SOLAR MERRY-GO-ROUND MODEL

This wire model of the nine known planets and the sun (without the comets and asteroids) will give a rough idea of the paths of the planets. Circles instead of ellipses are used because you can build them more easily.

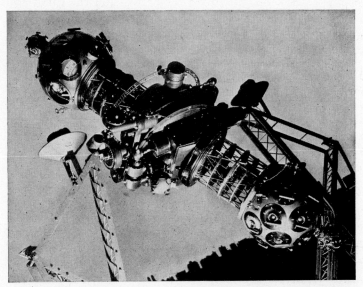

Fig. 27.—The planetarium machine at the Hayden Planetarium, New York City. (*Photograph, Courtesy American Museum of Natural History.*)

It is sometimes called an "orrery" because one of these was built for the Earl of Orrery in England (about A.D. 1700), who was very much interested in the stars. It might better be known as a planetarium because it shows the motion of the planets. A fine, large model of this type was built by the Father of American Astronomy, David Rittenhouse of Philadelphia, about 1760. You can see it in excellent condition if you visit the astronomy section of the Franklin Institute Museum in Philadelphia. These models of the solar system were the simple beginnings of the present planetarium, which is a "manufactured" sky with all the stars and planets moving as in the real sky. The planetarium machine which does this is awe-

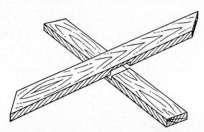

FIG. 28.—Notching of crosspieces.

inspiring and interesting, and is really a kind of motion-picture projector (see Fig. 27).

Materials. 100 feet of No. 16 gauge galvanized iron wire; 2 pieces of wood ½ by 30 inches; wood or steel balls of the following diameters: 1 ball, 4 inches; 1 ball, ¾ inch; 1 ball, ½ inch; 2 balls, ¼ inch; 3 balls, ⅛ inch; 2 balls ¹⁄₁₆ inch; box of copper tacks No. 8; 9 pieces of white cardboard 1 by 2 inches; and soldering equipment.

Directions.

1. Notch the two pieces of wood so that they form a cross (see Fig. 28).

2. Using the following dimensions, fasten 9 rows of tacks on each crosspiece. Solder the wire to the tacks. Dimensions from center for copper tacks to represent each planet's orbit: Mercury, 3½ inches; Jupiter, 6⅝ inches; Venus, 4 inches; Saturn, 7⅝ inches; earth, 4⅝ inches; Uranus, 11⅜ inches; Mars, 5⅜ inches; Neptune 12⅞ inches; and Pluto, 14 inches (see Fig. 29).

3. Burn or cut a slit groove on each ball. Use each ball to show the following: sun, 4 inches; Jupiter, ¾ inch; Saturn, ¾ inch;

Neptune, ¼ inch; Pluto, ⅟₁₆ inch; Uranus, ¼ inch; earth, ⅛ inch; Venus, ⅛ inch; Mars, about ⅟₁₆ inch; Mercury, about ⅟₁₆ inch.

4. Rest the slit of each ball on the proper wire orbit.

5. In the center of the crosspiece, fasten the ball representing the sun by driving a nail from the top down to the board.

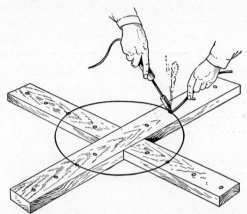

Fig. 29.—Soldering wire to tacks on crosspieces.

6. Paint each planet the following colors: Mercury, silver; Venus, yellow; earth, brown; Mars, red; Jupiter, silver; Saturn, red-yellow; Uranus, yellow; Neptune, blue; Pluto, yellow.

TABLE XII
SOLAR SYSTEM FACTS

Planets	Diameter, miles	Distance from sun, miles	Year	"Day"	Moons
Mercury...	3,009	35,950,000	88 days	88 days	
Venus.....	7,575	67,170,000	225 days	30 days	
Earth.....	7,918	92,870,000	365.26 days	23 hr. 56 min.	1
Mars......	4,216	141,498,000	687 days	24 hr. 37 min.	2
Jupiter.....	86,728	483,177,000	11.86 years	9 hr. 55 min.	9
Saturn.....	72,430	885,825,000	29.46 years	10 hr. 14 min.	9
Uranus....	30,878	1,782,151,000	84.02 years	10 hr. 45 min.	4
Neptune...	32,932	2,792,499,000	164.79 years	15 hr. 50 min.	1
Pluto......	2,000	3,700,000,000	248 years		

7. Paint the sun a bright red-orange.

8. On the 9 pieces of cardboard, write the facts from Table VIII about each planet. Tack these strips to the outer edges of the crosspiece.

TABLE XIII
MYTHOLOGY OF PLANETS

Planets	Mythology	Planets	Mythology
Mercury.........	God of Speed	Saturn.....	God of Harvest
Venus...........	Goddess of Beauty	Uranus.....	God of the Sky
Earth...........		Neptune....	God of the Sea
Mars............	God of War	Pluto......	God of the Under-
Jupiter..........	God of Heavens		world

9. Cut out a paper disk having a center hole slightly smaller than the ball representing Saturn. Glue this over Saturn and paint a yellow tint.

10. Make 9 paper arrowheads and glue each arrowhead on a wire circle. They should all point in the same direction, indicating the orbit and motion of each planet about the sun.

B. WHERE ARE THE WANDERING PLANETS?

Boys and girls who have fun watching the night sky are generally puzzled because they cannot point out the planets. They say, "I've read about the nine planets in the solar system; I know most of the constellations; I've been told that stars twinkle and that planets give a steady light and that the planets move while the stars do not; yet, I can't show my friends where the planets are because everything in the night sky looks alike. Besides, star charts and maps do not clearly show me where the planets are." So these puzzled boys and girls ask, "Where do I look for the wandering planets?"

In order to answer this question, you should first know that you can see only five planets with the naked eye. The planets Uranus, Neptune, and Pluto are so far away from the earth that you would need a telescope to see them. Mercury, the planet closest to the sun, never rises very high above the horizon and moves out of sight very quickly. Since you cannot see these planets without difficulty or a telescope, we will consider the other four planets in answering your question. These "naked-eye" planets, as they are called, are bright objects in the night sky.

To tell you where they are among the stars is not difficult if you remember that the planets move on a definite path through the sky (see page 12). They do not wander all over the star-filled sky but stay on a special track, called the zodiac. This zodiacal path passes "in front of" the 12 constellations discussed in Chapter II. As each planet journeys across the sky, it passes in front of one of the constellations. Then astronomers say that it is *in* that constellation.

This can be explained in another way by asking you a question. Have you been across the street from a large department store, or row of stores, which had many display windows and watched someone walk in front of those windows? You could tell a blind person where that walker was by saying that he had passed in front of a certain window. The planets are found in the same way as they travel in the sky in front of each of the 12 zodiacal constellations. Thus, if astronomers say that Jupiter is in Sagittarius or that Mars is in Scorpius, you will understand that you can see these planets as they are moving in that part of the sky where Sagittarius or Scorpius is located. By this time you should be able to point to the 12 zodiacal constellations if you have read Chapter II. Of course, if the planet is moving in a constellation which is not visible at night, then the planet cannot be seen either.

To actually notice the planets moving across the stars in the zodiacal constellations, you will have to observe them night after night for several weeks, or even several months. Then, if you have made star charts of the constellations (see Chapter III), you can compare their outlines with the real ones in the heavens. If you see a very bright "star" which is not on your chart, you can be sure it is the planet you are looking for.

While the planets move in the general direction of west to east on the path of the zodiac, they travel oddly at certain times. You should know about these doings because you are apt to become confused unless you are prepared for them.

Our near neighbor Venus is sometimes seen in the east an hour or so before sunrise and sometimes in the west about an hour after sunset. Venus is called the Morning Star or the Evening Star, depending upon the time it is visible in the sky. You may have heard people refer to it by these names. When it is scheduled to appear as an evening star, Venus may be seen above the western horizon right after sunset. Then, from night to night, for a period of nine and one-half months it will climb in the sky, moving in front of one of the zodiacal constellations. When it reaches a point about halfway overhead (48 degrees), the planet starts sinking back toward the horizon and disappears. Then if you want to see Venus, you will have to look for it in the morning sky, where it will go through the same climbing and sinking. Because Venus is brighter than any other sky object, except the sun and the moon, you should be able to point it out very easily among the stars in the constellation.

Mars, Jupiter, and Saturn go along in a more orderly fashion; they do not jump back and forth as Venus does. However, every so often, they stop this regular west to east motion and act almost as queerly as Venus. Suppose we follow one of the "bright four" on one of its irregular journeys. Let us say that early one evening you first saw Mars in Libra just to the right (west) of Antares (see page 36). Then night after night, you went out and watched this bright red planet slowly pass to the left (east) of Antares. From what was said about the planets, you would expect Mars to keep on going from Libra toward Scorpius. Instead, Mars seems to pause for a night or so and then swings *backward* toward the west. That is, it moves back to where it was a month or so before. Mars does this backtracking for about two months. Then it makes up its mind to do what it started out to do; it begins to go east just as any well-behaved planet should do. This backward motion of Mars is called "retrogression" by astronomers. While it is well understood today, the retrogression of Mars caused the ancient astronomers many headaches because they could not explain this peculiar traveling.

Jupiter and Saturn also pass along the zodiacal constellations just as Mars does. While Jupiter and Saturn also retrogress, you cannot see this backtracking happen as quickly as when Mars is moving. Jupiter takes about four months and Saturn not quite five months to retrogress.

As you watch Mars in its wandering, notice its deep red color. Observe, also, that Saturn has a yellowish-red tinge and Jupiter is a silver-white color. If you should go out a short while after sunset, you should be able to pick out any of the four bright planets. You may see them a little while before your eyes can pick out the stars.

In order that you may know in what constellations the planets are moving, Tables XIV to XVII are given for the years 1946 to 1949, inclusive.

You may use the tables in two ways: (1) to find the constellation in which to look for a planet, and (2) to find what planet, or planets, are in a given constellation. For example, suppose the date were May, 1946, and you wanted to know where to point to the planet Mars. On the 1946 table, look down the May column for Mars. When you find it, look over to the left-hand column for the zodiacal constellation. This happens to be Cancer. Turn to page 28, in Chapter II, for pointing direction for this constellation. Locating the position of Cancer, you can easily point to Mars. Suppose, on the other hand, you wanted to know what planet was in Gemini for the same time, May, 1946. Again refer to the table for 1946 and in the left-hand column find Gemini. Then look to

TABLE XIV

THE POSITION OF THE PLANETS IN THE CONSTELLATIONS OF THE ZODIAC
1946

Constellation	Jan.	Feb.	March	April	May	June	July	Aug.	Sept.	Oct.	Nov.	Dec.
Aries												
Taurus					Venus							
Gemini	Mars Saturn	Mars Saturn	Mars Saturn	Saturn	Saturn	Saturn Venus			Saturn	Saturn	Saturn	Saturn
Cancer				Mars	Mars							
Leo						Mars	Venus Mars					
Virgo	Jupiter	Jupiter	Jupiter	Jupiter	Jupiter	Jupiter	Jupiter	Jupiter Mars Venus	Jupiter Mars			
Libra									Venus	Mars		Venus Jupiter
Scorpius										Venus	Mars	
Sagittarius												
Capricornus												
Aquarius												
Pisces												

TABLE XV
THE POSITION OF THE PLANETS IN THE CONSTELLATIONS OF THE ZODIAC
1947

Constellation	Jan.	Feb.	March	April	May	June	July	Aug.	Sept.	Oct.	Nov.	Dec.
Aries						Mars						
Taurus							Mars	Mars				
Gemini									Mars	Mars		
Cancer	Saturn	Saturn	Saturn	Saturn	Saturn	Saturn						
Leo									Saturn	Saturn	Mars Saturn	Mars Saturn
Virgo												
Libra	Jupiter					Jupiter	Jupiter	Jupiter	Jupiter			
Scorpius		Jupiter	Jupiter	Jupiter	Jupiter					Jupiter		
Sagittarius	Venus	Venus										
Capricornus			Venus	Venus								Venus
Aquarius		Mars	Mars									
Pisces				Mars	Mars Venus							

Table XVI

THE POSITION OF THE PLANETS IN THE CONSTELLATIONS OF THE ZODIAC

1948

Constellation	Jan.	Feb.	March	April	May	June	July	Aug.	Sept.	Oct.	Nov.	Dec.
Aries												
Taurus			Venus	Venus			Venus					
Gemini					Venus			Venus				
Cancer									Venus			
Leo	Mars Saturn	Mars Saturn	Mars Saturn	Mars Saturn	Mars Saturn	Mars Saturn	Saturn			Venus Saturn	Saturn	Saturn
Virgo							Mars	Mars			Venus	
Libra									Mars			
Scorpius										Mars		Venus
Sagittarius	Jupiter	Jupiter	Jupiter	Jupiter	Jupiter	Jupiter	Jupiter	Jupiter	Jupiter	Jupiter	Jupiter Mars	Mars
Capricornus												
Aquarius	Venus											
Pisces		Venus										

Table XVII
THE POSITION OF THE PLANETS IN THE CONSTELLATIONS OF THE ZODIAC
1949

Constellation	Jan.	Feb.	March	April	May	June	July	Aug.	Sept.	Oct.	Nov.	Dec.
Aries					Mars							
Taurus						Mars	Mars					
Gemini								Mars				
Cancer									Mars			
Leo	Saturn	Saturn	Saturn	Saturn	Saturn	Saturn	Venus Saturn			Mars Saturn	Mars Saturn	Mars Saturn
Virgo								Venus				
Libra									Venus			
Scorpius										Venus		
Sagittarius		Jupiter	Jupiter								Venus	
Capricornus	Mars			Jupiter	Jupiter	Jupiter	Jupiter	Jupiter	Jupiter	Jupiter	Jupiter	Venus Jupiter
Aquarius		Mars										
Pisces												

★ 135 ★

the right until you are under the May column. You will find that Gemini has the planet Saturn in it.

If you have built the solar "merry-go-round" model on page 125, you can add a few things to it which will show the wandering of the planets. You can then control the motion of the planets as the planetarium does. With this added attachment, the retrogression of the planets becomes a simple matter. In fact, your knowledge of the wandering planets will be even greater than that of the ancient astronomers.

ADVANCED ACTIVITY B. HOW TO MAKE THE SOLAR MERRY-GO-ROUND INTO A PLANETARIUM

Materials. Solar system merry-go-round model; heavy cardboard; paste and tacks.

Directions.

1. Cut the cardboard into long strips 2 inches wide.
2. Paste these strips together to form a strip 96 inches long.
3. Draw a heavy black pencil line across the long strip, every 8 inches. There will be 12 divisions.
4. Draw the outline figure of the 12 zodiacal constellations (see page 27) in each 8-inch section. Start with Aries at one end and continue to Pisces (see Fig. 30).
5. Tack the long cardboard strip to the ends of the crosspiece of the merry-go-round model. This should make a circle parallel to the orbits.
6. Move the planet-balls so that each is in front of the correct constellation as you sight from the earth. (See Tables XIV to XVII for position of Venus, Mars, Jupiter, and Saturn.) For all practical purposes, Uranus may be considered to be in Aries; Neptune to be in Leo; and Pluto in Gemini. Mercury makes a little over four revolutions around the sun to each revolution of the earth.
7. As the earth changes its position in one month, move Mars (or Jupiter, or Saturn) its equal part of one of our months.
8. Sight from the earth through any one of the planets (Mars, for instance) to the constellation in the background.
9. Mark the position of Mars with chalk on the cardboard.

★ 136 ★

10. Repeat 12 times, representing the earth's 12 months in its year of revolution.

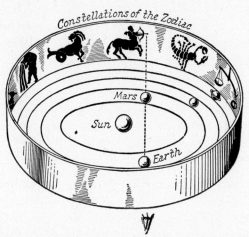

Fig. 30.—Planet positions in merry-go-round model with face sighting from earth through Mars to star background

ADVANCED READING ACTIVITY

Barton, William H., Jr.: *World Wide Planisphere*. Cambridge, Mass., Addison-Wesley Press, Inc., 1944.

Lowell, Percival: *Mars*. Boston, Houghton Mifflin Company, 1895.

Menzel, D. H.: *Stars and Planets*. New York, The University Society, Inc., 1935.

The Observer's Handbook (annual). The Royal Astronomical Society of Canada, 198 College St., Toronto, Canada.

Publication of the Carnegie Institution, Washington, D. C. (Free to schools.)

Russell, H. N.: *The Solar System and Its Origin*. New York, The Macmillan Company, 1935.

Sky and Telescope (monthly). Harvard College Observatory, Cambridge, Mass.

Whipple, Fred L.: *Earth, Moon and Planets*. Philadelphia, The Blakiston Company, 1941.

☆

★ VII ★

☆

Getting Away Out into Space

You learned in Chapter VI that the most distant planet, Pluto, discovered in 1930, is 3,700,000,000 miles away from the sun! This means that the closest we on the world can come to Pluto is about 3,000,000,000 miles. At other times, the world is many millions of miles farther away from Pluto, depending upon the positions in the orbits. If these distances are written out in numbers, they become staggering to the human mind. Yet astronomers tell us that the *nearest* star is many thousand times farther away from the earth. They also inform us that these tremendous distances in miles are small compared to the distances of nebulae and clusters. These are so far away that their distances must be measured in light-years. A light-year equals nearly six trillion miles (6,000,000,-000,000). (See page 148.) A reasoning boy or girl rightfully asks, "How can astronomers measure those distances to the stars and planets, when they can't leave the earth?"

The answer to this question is found in mathematics, which astronomers have developed so that they can measure these distances with a high degree of accuracy. They can also predict solar eclipses to within a few seconds. This book is not the proper place to go into details of the higher mathematics, but the method used by astronomers can be explained simply.

In Chapter VIII, you will see how sun time is measured with the shadow of upright objects. In our explanation, we will use a similar idea, your body being the shadow maker. Sometime in your life you may have wanted to know the height of a high tree, pole, or building. You could have found the answer by comparing the length of your shadow to the shadow length of a tree, pole, or building, coming from the same source of light. The answer would be the height of the tree, pole, or building, which you do not have to climb to measure. Do the following activity, if you want to understand this method.

ACTIVITY A. HOW TO MEASURE DISTANCES WITH SHADOWS

Directions.

1. Choose a tree, pole, or building which is casting a sharp shadow.

2. Measure the length of the shadow from the base of the object.

3. Stand near the object so that your body casts a shadow in the same direction as the object.

4. Measure the length of your shadow.

5. Divide this number into the length of the shadow No. 2.

6. Multiply this answer by your *actual* height.

7. The answer will be the height of the unreachable object.

For example, suppose a flag pole had cast a shadow 80 feet long when your shadow measured 8 feet. If your height is 5 feet, you can write this equation:

$$\frac{80}{8} = \frac{x}{5}; \text{ then } x = 50 \text{ feet}$$

Your brain went up to the top of the flag pole while your body stayed on the ground. You measured a space distance without leaving the ground!

If you have made the cross-staff in Chapter V, page 102, you can have much fun using the instrument measuring tall objects and "hard-to-get-at" places around the schoolyard or in your neighborhood. While you are doing this, you will learn another way in which astronomers work on measurement problems.

ACTIVITY B. HOW TO USE THE CROSS-STAFF FOR DIMENSIONS

Material. Cross-staff made as shown on page 102, adding-machine paper 36 inches long, ruler, and pencil.

Directions.

1. Draw a center line down the length of the adding-machine paper. Label one part "50 feet" and the other "100 feet."

2. Beginning at the eye end of the paper, draw lines across the width of paper at the following distances:

TABLE XVIII
CROSS-STAFF LAYOUT

Inches	Inches	Inches	Inches	Inches	Inches	Inches	Inches
6.0	6.7	7.5	8.6	10.0	12.0	15.0	21.4
6.1	6.8	7.7	8.8	10.3	12.5	15.8	23.1
6.2	7.0	7.9	9.1	10.7	13.0	16.7	25.0
6.4	7.1	8.1	9.4	11.1	13.6	17.7	27.3
6.5	7.3	8.4	9.7	11.5	14.3	20.0	30.0

3. In corresponding blocks, fill in dimensions from the following table; these will be the heights or widths of the measured objects.

TABLE XIX
CROSS-STAFF DIMENSIONS FOR SIZE

Fifty-foot column							
50 feet	45 feet	40 feet	35 feet	30 feet	25 feet	20 feet	15 feet
49	44	39	34	29	24	19	14
48	43	38	33	28	23	18	13
47	42	37	32	27	22	17	12
46	41	36	31	26	21	16	11

TABLE XX
CROSS-STAFF DIMENSIONS FOR SIZE

100-foot column

100 feet	90 feet	80 feet	70 feet	60 feet	50 feet	40 feet	30 feet
98	88	78	68	58	48	38	28
96	86	76	66	56	46	36	26
94	84	74	64	54	44	34	24
92	82	72	62	52	42	32	22

4. Paste this paper on the uncovered side of the cross-staff.

5. Measure (by walking) either 50 feet or 100 feet away from the object.

6. Press the eye end of the staff against your cheek. Aim at the object to be measured.

7. Slide the crosspiece back and forth until its edges just cover the ends of the object (see Fig. 18, page 103).

8. Press the crosspiece against the staff.

9. Read the dimension on the eye side of the scale. *The number will be the height or width of the object in feet.*

10. Using the same method, find the height of (*a*) the flag pole; (*b*) the school building; (*c*) a telegraph pole; (*d*) a tall tree; (*e*) your house.

11. It is suggested that you use the 50-foot scale for objects having dimensions between 10 feet and 50 feet; and the 100-foot scale for objects between 30 feet and 100 feet.

If you have made and used the cross-staff (Activity B, page 140) you should see how it is possible to measure indirectly the distance to an inaccessible object. Without going into the details of the mathematics, you should understand that by measuring *one* distance on the earth (called the base line), and using the geometry of angles, it is not difficult to figure out measurements. In the cross-staff activity, the base line was the 50-foot or 100-foot distance which you walked and measured from the object. In addition, there was one angle which your eyes observed along the edges of the crosspiece.

The authors of this book calculated the dimensions in the two columns above by using mathematics.

This is all the information needed by an astronomer or mathematician to solve a distance or dimension problem. The same simple principle was used by the Greek mathematician, Eratosthenes, about 200 B.C., in estimating the circumference of the earth to be 25,000 miles. Eratosthenes used the known distance, 500 miles, between the Egyptian cities, Syene (now Aswan) and Alexandria, as his base line; for the two angles, he knew that the sun was directly overhead (90 degrees) at Syene on June 21, while at Alexandria, he found that the sun was about 7 degrees 12 minutes south of overhead. Thus, with this base distance and two angles, he measured 25,000 miles without walking a mile from Alexandria (see Fig. 31)!

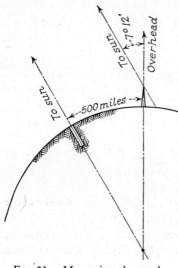

Fig. 31.—Measuring the earth.

Another way to illustrate this idea is to hold something before your eyes and look at a large distant object. If you use the palm of your hand and gaze at a house across the street, your small hand (about 3 to 4 inches) will make the large house (about 16 to 25 feet) disappear. You can do the same thing with a coin, dime, nickel, or penny. The odd thing about these small pieces of money is that they can be used in a crude way to tell how far away a large object is. For example, if you hold a penny at arm's length and look at it with one open eye, you can cover a small boy or girl at a distance of over 200 feet. As the distance between you and the object becomes greater, you can cover wider or taller objects. Try this!

★ 142 ★

Gradually astronomers learned that a base line of 500 miles was too small for measuring to a distant object like the moon, or sun, and was entirely unsatisfactory for the stars. But they knew they could measure space distances, if they could get larger base lines (see Fig. 32). The 8,000-mile diameter of

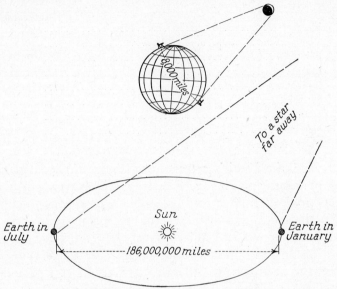

Fig. 32.—Large and small base lines.

the earth and the diameter of the earth's orbit, which is double the distance of the earth to the sun (186,000,000 miles), were next used. These larger base lines enabled astronomers to measure the solar system and star distances (see page 146).

The tremendous distances, in millions of miles, soon became too clumsy for constant use and a new kind of ruler had to be invented which was more suitable. You would not use an inch as the right ruler to measure the distance between New York and Chicago, because it is too small. For the same reason, the astronomers agreed to use the distance from the earth to the sun (93,000,000 miles) as the new ruler. They called this one "astronomical unit." The table gives the

★ 143 ★

distances to the planets in astronomical units (see page 127 for these distances in miles).

PLANET DISTANCES IN ASTRONOMICAL UNITS

Planet	Distance from Sun in Astronomical Units (A.U.)
Mercury	0.4
Venus	0.7
Earth	1.0
Mars	1.5
Jupiter	5.2
Saturn	9.5
Uranus	19.1
Neptune	30.0
Pluto	39.5

In 1675 the Danish astronomer Römer stumbled upon a way of measuring the speed of light by observing that the inner moon of Jupiter took 22 minutes more to be eclipsed when the earth was farthest away from Jupiter. While his actual answer was not quite correct, he started astronomers working on the same problem. Later, they found the speed of light to be about 186,000 miles per second. This gave them another convenient ruler to measure distances to the stars. It is called a "light-year" and is equal to a little less than six trillion miles. You can see that this ruler would be too large for distances to the planets because even Pluto, the most distant planet known, would be less than 1/1,500 of a light-year away from us!

The distance to any near-by star is measured by observing how much it appears to change its position in an interval of six months against a background of more distant stars. This can be explained if you look at one finger held at arm's length before your eyes. Close one eye and sight at the background. Then quickly close that eye and open the other, not moving the finger. Your finger appears to "jump" before your eye! Yet you had not moved it. The amount that your finger jumps, or changes position is large and can be measured in angles, because the base line is the distance between your eyes (see Fig. 33). A star, because it is so far away, appears to move a very small amount against the background of the distant stars. This slight change is called "displacement" or "parallax." It is so small (tenths or hundredths of one second of angle) that sensitive instruments must be attached to large telescopes to measure or photograph it. The parallax is sometimes measured in units called "parsecs," a combination of "parallax" and "second" of an angle. The observations are made six months apart in order to produce a very large base line—the diameter of the earth's orbit which is equal to 186,000,000 miles. That is, we observe the same star from two positions in space on the base line, thus measuring space without leaving the earth!

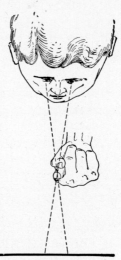

Fig. 33.—Illustration of parallax.

In your early schooling, you learned that there are 12 inches to a foot, 3 feet in a yard, and 5,280 feet or 1,760 yards in a mile. Astronomers' rulers can be expressed in the same way. Thus:

(About) 93,000,000 miles = 1 astronomical unit (A.U.)
(About) 62,300 A.U. = 1 light-year (L.Y.)
3.26 L.Y. = 1 parsec

As you look at the constellation, pick out the star whose distance is given in the above table. What you are seeing is the "past," or history. That is, the light that hits your eyes started from that star as many years ago as the number shows. Some boys and girls like to set down the events which happened in history alongside of the light-year distances. This makes them feel as if they had a ringside seat at the march of history. For example, as you gaze at Procyon (see page 80) in Canis Minor which is 10.5 light-years away, think back where you were and what was happening 10 years ago. Both

(see page 80)

TABLE XXII

DISTANCES OF THE BRIGHTER STARS*

Name	Constellation	Distance, light-years away from earth
Alcor	Ursa Major	72
Alcyone	Taurus	465
Aldebaran	Taurus	54
Algol	Perseus	109
Alioth	Ursa Major	72
Alkaid	Ursa Major	326
Alpheratz	Andromeda	99
Altair	Aquila	15.5
Antares	Scorpius	163
Arcturus	Boötes	36
Bellatrix	Orion	217
Betelgeuse	Orion	272
Capella	Auriga	44
Castor	Gemini	44
Deneb	Cygnus	652
Denebola	Leo	43
Fomalhaut	Piscis Austrinus	25
Markab	Pegasus	93
Mira	Cetus	251
Mizar	Ursa Major	77
Polaris	Ursa Minor	465
Pollux	Gemini	33
Procyon	Canis Minor	10.5
Regulus	Leo	72
Rigel	Orion	543
Schedar	Cassiopeia	191
Sirius	Canis Major	8.6
Spica	Virgo	204
Vega	Lyra	25

* From Barton and Barton: *A Guide to the Constellations*. Whittlesey House, McGraw-Hill Book Company, Inc., New York.

the event and the star light happened at the same time. But the event is history, while the starlight is now, or the present. Again the light from Antares in Scorpius (see page 36) started to come to us about the time George Washington was struggling to make this country a republic. Yet Washington is history, while the light from Antares is *just* reaching your eye. In other words, when you are observing the stars, you are really "seeing the past." To see what the stars are now, you must wait the number of years that they are away from us! Some you will never live to see! For instance, Betelgeuse in Orion (see page 78) at this moment is sending forth light that will strike the eyes of the future generations, 272 years from now (A.D. 1946 to A.D. 2218). The constellation description in Chapter II gives other objects for you to look at and think about. Clusters, gaseous nebulae, and spiral nebulae are indeed the future! Be curious! Turn back to Chapter II and pick out these distant universes. Step outside at night and marvel at Divine Providence!

Some of the larger stars have been measured, although astronomers frankly say that the diameters of the giant stars are the only ones they can measure. They caution us to under-

TABLE XXIII
DIAMETER OF STARS

Name	Millions of Miles
Arcturus	23
Aldebaran	33
β Pegasi (Scheat)	35
Betelgeuse	180–260
Mira	220
α Herculis	350
Antares	390

stand that even these measurements are not really accurate. Table XXIII gives the diameter of a few stars in millions of miles.

In order that you may get a better idea of the vast size of these stars, suppose you look at the sun. This is 93,000,000 miles away. Yet the diameter of Betelgeuse in Orion is at least twice the distance from the earth to the sun! Antares in Scorpius is so tremendous in diameter that the sun can be placed in its center with Mercury, Venus, earth, and Mars rolling around in their respective orbits with plenty of space to spare! When you gaze at these giant stars tonight, think of these facts. What a small speck upon a tiny dot in a small "world" system is man with his weak body, curious brain, and brave imagination.

ACTIVITY C.   CRAZY NUMBERS

Some boys and girls enjoy setting down numbers and multiplying them. Astronomers' rulers can be used for this interesting activity. Multiplication produces numbers so long that they have been called "crazy numbers." At the same time, the actual number value of these distances in terms of what we are accustomed to see is so vast that people become reverent.

Materials. Blackboard or scratch pad, chalk or pencil.

Directions.

1. Write the number of the speed of light (186,000 miles per second).

2. Multiply this by 60 (seconds in a minute).

3. Multiply this answer by 60 (minutes in an hour).

4. Multiply this answer by 24 (hours in a day).

5. Multiply this answer by 365¼ (days in a year).

6. The answer is number of miles in a light-year.

7. Figure out the time it takes for light to reach the earth from: (*a*) the moon; (*b*) sun; (*c*) each planet; (*d*) nearest star (Alpha Centauri); (*e*) the Milky Way; (*f*) Andromeda Nebula.

8. Compute the number of miles that each star on page 146 is away from the earth.

You notice how large these numbers become. Astronomers are careful to point out that in measuring distances farther and farther away, the figure that they must work with is liable to a large error. This makes the result little better than a good guess. To bore into the depths of space, it is necessary to use another method besides parallax. This is described in more advanced textbooks on astronomy.

ADVANCED READING ACTIVITY

Duncan, V. C.: *Astronomy*. New York, Harper & Brothers, 1935.

Gray, George W.: *New World Picture*. Boston, Little, Brown and Company, 1936.

Hubble, Edwin: *The Realm of the Nebulae*. New Haven, Yale University Press, 1936.

Jeans, Sir James: *The Mysterious Universe*. New York, The Macmillan Company, 1935.

Shapley, Harlow, and Helen E. Howarth: *A Source Book in Astronomy*. New York, McGraw-Hill Book Company, Inc., 1929.

VIII

Shadowing Time

THE SUNDIAL

MUCH has been written about the way government detec-tives shadow a crime suspect by trailing him day and night. Daily, astronomers trail the stars and the shadow of the sun to track down an accurate measure of something we can use to register the events of life—Time. The old Greeks pictured Time as an old man-god carrying an hour glass and a scythe. They called him Chronos, from which our scientific watches and clocks get their name chronometers, meaning "measurer of time."

The sun moves across the sky each day and when clouds do not interfere it regularly makes shadows on the earth. The sun, of course, only appears to be moving, whereas, as you learned in geography, this earth upon which we live rotates daily upon its axis from west to east. For time's sake it will not be unreasonable, however, to consider the sun moving from east to west and to think of the earth being stationary. If you could go out somewhere in space and see the spinning earth, it would be the best watch in the universe because it rotates *regularly*. Since you cannot do this, you must find a substitute; a good one is the regular daily journey of the sun casting shadows upon the earth.

Old astronomers learned that slender, upright objects made shadows with circular paths which could be trailed easily and accurately. They used sticks, trees, piles of rock, and poles to cause the sun to cast a shadow. They called these "gnomons," or "shadow makers." By dividing the shadow path into equal parts, they had a rough estimate of time.

Suppose you trail the sun's shadow and see how the old astronomers struggled and worried to catch up on Father Time. Today we accept accurately timed railroads, steamships, airplanes, and radio programs as ordinary things. By following the directions in the next few activities, you should appreciate the problems of telling the time by shadowing the sun.

ACTIVITY A. HOW TO SHADOW THE SUN

Materials. Heavy cardboard (size, to fit a window frame tightly); box of thumb tacks.

Directions.

Fig. 34.—Student making an inside analemma, or shadowing the sun.

1. Choose a window which is always in the sunlight.
2. Make a small hole (½ inch) in the center of the cardboard.

3. Fasten the cardboard to the inside of the window frame so that it cannot be dislodged.

4. As early as possible in the morning, observe the spot of sunlight which comes through the cardboard. Place a thumbtack over the spot.

5. At the end of each hour (or whenever convenient) cover the new spot with a tack (see Fig. 34).

6. At the end of the day, remove the tacks and draw a line connecting the tack holes.

7. Label the date on this line.

FIG. 35.—Making an outside analemma.

8. Repeat this activity for at least a month.

9. Pick out the spot where noon occurs. (When the sun crosses the meridian line which is true north and south.)

OUTSIDE ACTIVITY B.   HOW TO TIME THE SUN'S SHADOW

Materials. Broomstick about 3 feet (or equal length of about 1-inch lumber); tacks; short piece of string; iron washer; 12 checker pieces or stones; piece of chalk.

Directions.

1. Choose a clear, unobstructed plot of ground which is always in the sunlight.

2. On the stick, make a plumb line out of the string and washer.

3. Drive the stick into the ground.

4. Adjust the stick so that the iron washer lies flat against it and the string is in the center of the stick.

★ 152 ★

5. As early as possible in the morning, observe the stick's shadow.

6. Place a checker piece or stone at the end of this shadow (see Fig. 35).

7. At the end of each hour (or whenever convenient) place another checker or stone.

8. Continue placing these markers until the sun has set or until you cannot see the shadow of the stick.

9. Draw a curved line connecting the markers for that day. Date this line.

10. Label the hour places of the shadow.

11. Repeat this activity for a week or more.

More than likely, you have noticed a few interesting things in doing the above activities. You may have noticed that the sun shadow on the floor or ground does not fall on the same place for the same hour each day. If you continued shadowing the sun for about a month, you would notice that the noon shadow moves either forward or backward. This shadow moving is caused by the sun traveling north or south.

In either of these activities, you notice that the end of the shadow makes a distinct trail which forms a sort of semicircle. You can divide the sun's semicircle shadow into 12 equal parts, and call each division an hour. This is a crude form of a sundial or sun clock.

In the latitudes of the United States, in order to make the sun's shadow fall on the same place at the same hour each day, it is necessary to slant the gnomon toward the northern horizon so that it will be leaning over the ground at an angle equal to the latitude. Otherwise, the sun's shadow would show the same hour on a different spot every day. We do not know who first discovered this fact, but it is certain that sundials are very old instruments for telling the time of the day.

We owe our modern sundial with its hour markings to the unceasing trailing of the sun shadow by the ancient Greeks,

Egyptians, and Babylonians. The Greeks borrowed from the earlier Babylonians the incorrect method of dividing the day into 12 hours by stating that the sun always rose at 6 A.M. and set at 6 P.M. This caused an hour in the summer to be longer than in the winter. Think how this would lengthen your vacation afternoon, but also think how this would shorten the hours of your favorite sport during fall and winter afternoons! Our present system of dividing the day into 24 equal hours, winter and summer, is an old Egyptian idea. This causes the sun to rise before six in the summer, and after six in the winter.

An Egyptian dial of 1500 B.C. was shaped like a reclining L

FIG. 36.—Modern wall sundial. (*Elizabeth S. Kugler.*)

and turned toward the east in the morning and toward the west after the sun had crossed the meridian. This dial told the hours when the sun's shadow passed over spaced lines. The Bible mentions the sundial of Ahaz (about 742 B.C.) in the second book of Kings 20: 8, 11, and Isaiah 38: 8. The Greek astronomer Anaximander (about 544 B.C.) built a gnomon in Sparta, as the basis of a crude sundial which the records show that he obtained from older Babylonians as early as 1100 B.C. The obelisks built by Emperor Augustus in Rome (about 20 B.C.) were no doubt used as gnomons of sundials. The pyramids of Egypt are also thought to have been used for this purpose because they cast such large shadows. Berossus, a Chaldean astronomer (about 270 B.C.), was an expert dial maker and clearly understood the necessity of slanting the gnomon to the latitude angle to get correct sun time. Even in Peru and Mexico, where recorded history is not plentiful, there are many ruins of sundials. On the weathered stones of old English churches are the dim, and sometimes distinct, lines of scratch dials upon which the sun's shadow indicated the hours of church services. The beautiful wall dial on the Bok Singing Tower in Florida is shown in Fig. 36.

Perhaps you have noticed that sundials have been appearing more frequently in beautiful modern gardens and landscapes. Some have been placed upon birdbaths while others are fastened to stone or cement pedestals. Many schools have the pedestal type on their lawns. They are usually decorated with some apt motto or poem. The dial, of course, will tell sun time, which is slightly inaccurate clock time.

The next section of activities will be devoted to specific directions for making a horizontal or vertical sundial of special size. Why don't you make a sundial for your home? Maybe your club can get together and build one for your schoolyard or school wall. It will be fun and you can use this "sun clock" during recess or lunch hour. Or your summer camp should have a dial. It is advisable for you to experiment with wood or cardboard before you try to make brass, bronze, or cement sundials.

ACTIVITY C. HOW TO MAKE A HORIZONTAL SUNDIAL
(8 BY 8 INCHES)

(FOR 40 DEGREES NORTH LATITUDE)

Materials. 8- by 8- by ½-inch wooden board (this must be exact); cardboard, 5 by 5 inches; ruler; glue; small wire nails.

Directions.

1. Across the board, draw a line 4 inches from the top. This is the base line.

2. Draw a center line to this line. This is the gnomon line.

3. Lay off the following dimensions from the gnomon line (see Fig. 36):

K and L............................ $1\frac{1}{16}$ inches
J and N............................ $1\frac{7}{16}$ inches
H and T............................ $2\frac{7}{16}$ inches

★ 155 ★

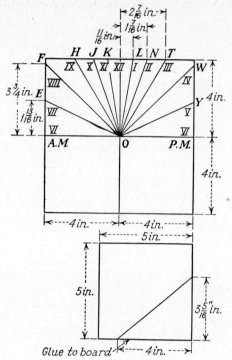

FIG. 37.—Layout of sundial.

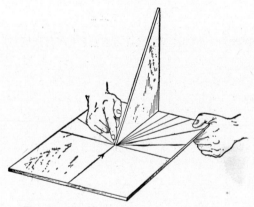

FIG. 38.—Fastening gnomon to dial plate.

★ 156 ★

4. From the base line, lay off the following dimensions:

E and Y............................. $1^{13}/_{16}$ inches

F and W............................. $3^{3}/_{4}$ inches

5. From the intersection of the gnomon line and the base line (at 0), draw straight lines to the above points.

6. Cut the cardboard so that it will form a triangle of the following dimensions: base, 4 inches; one side, $3^{5}/_{16}$ inches; other side, $5^{3}/_{4}$ inches.

7. Glue the triangular cardboard with the $3^{5}/_{16}$-inch side to the wooden board (see Fig. 38).

8. Mark the lines V, IV, III, II, I.

9. Mark the gnomon line XII, NOON.

10. Mark the right base line VI, P.M.

11. Mark the left base line VI, A.M.

12. Mark the next 5 lines VII, VIII, IX, X, XI.

13. Set the sundial on a flat surface.

14. Set the gnomon so that it points directly north and south (see Teacher or Guide).

15. When the sun's shadow touches any line, that is the hour of the day. When the shadow is between the lines, it is after the earlier hour; that is, if the shadow is halfway between IX and X, it is 9:30 A.M.

ACTIVITY D. HOW TO MAKE A VERTICAL SUNDIAL (8 BY 8 INCHES)

(FOR 40 DEGREES NORTH LATITUDE)

Materials. Same as horizontal.

Directions. Same as horizontal with the following exceptions.

1. Dimensions to lay off from the gnomon line (see Fig. 39):

K and L............................. $1^{3}/_{16}$ inches

J and N............................. $1^{3}/_{4}$ inches

H and T............................. 3 inches

2. Dimensions from base line:

E and Y............................. $1^{5}/_{8}$ inches

F and W............................. $3^{3}/_{16}$ inches

★ 157 ★

3. The triangular cardboard (the gnomon) shall be of the following dimensions: base, 4 inches; one side, 4⅝ inches; other side, 6³⁄₁₆ inches.

4. Glue the gnomon with the 4⅝-inch side to the board.

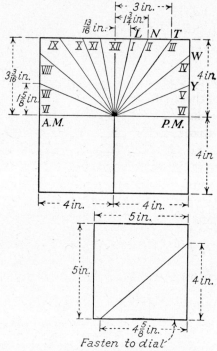

Fig. 39.—Vertical dial.

5. Suspend or fasten vertically against a post or side of a building facing south (see Fig. 36, page 154).

6. The gnomon should point directly N and S.

7. While these dials are designed for 8- by 8-inch dimensions, you can make them larger by merely extending the lines to the size you want.

If you will take the trouble to compare the sundial with your watch, you will discover that they do not agree exactly, except on four days in the year. These dates are April 15, June 15, September 1, and December 26. Sometimes the clock runs ahead of the dial and sometimes it gets behind. This is because the earth does not move *around the sun* at a regular pace, and because at noon in the summer the sun is higher in the sky than it is in the winter. The difference between clock time and the dial time is called "the equation of time." The clock is never more than 14 minutes faster than the dial, and the dial is never more than 16 minutes faster than the clock.

Maybe you have seen a peculiar diagram like a big "8" on globes of the earth. The figure is known as an "analemma" and shows the dates of the year when clock time is faster or slower than sundial time. You can make one of these diagrams or rather let it make itself. You will be interested in watching it "grow" during the part of the year you are at school or camp. Although you should let the analemma grow for a whole year, you will be satisfied with part of the analemma figure.

ACTIVITY E. THE ANALEMMA

Materials. Same as Activity A (see page 151).
Directions.
Same as Activity A with following additions:
1. Each day at exactly 12 o'clock noon (clock time) mark the sun spot on the floor.
2. Put a thumbtack on this spot.
3. At the first day of each month, use three tacks, an extra one on each side of the "spot" tack.
4. On the fifteenth of each month, use one extra tack to the right of the spot tack.
5. Number the tacks in rotation and keep a record of these dates.
6. Don't worry if you miss a day when it is cloudy or over the week ends. Fill in the missing days with tacks where the noon sun spot seems to follow the connecting line.
7. At the end of the year, you will notice the tacks look like a long figure 8. Compare your analemma with the earth globe.
8. Repeat this with the directions given in Activity B, page 152, for outside experiment.

The next tabulation will give the minute correction to be used with the sundial for 15-day intervals in each month on the stated dates. This was taken from an analemma. If you cannot do this activity, the table will show you the difference between dial time and clock time. It is the equation of time and you need it if you want accurate clock time from the sundial.

TABLE XXIV
EQUATION OF TIME

Add these minutes to the sundial time on:		Subtract these minutes from the sundial time on:	
Jan. 1 3M.	Jan. 15 9M.	May 1 2M.	May 15 4M.
Feb. 1 14M.	Feb. 15 14M.	June 1 2M.	June 15 0M.
Mar. 1 13M.	Mar. 15 9M.	Sept. 1 0M.	Sept. 15 5M.
Apr. 1 4M.	Apr. 15 0M.	Oct. 1 10M.	Oct. 15 14M.
July 1 4M.	July 15 6M.	Nov. 2 16M.	Nov. 15 15M.
Aug. 1 6M.	Aug. 15 4M.	Dec. 1 11M.	Dec. 15 5M.
		Dec. 25 0M.	

A sundial needs "dressing up." A dial is not finished until you add a touch of poetry. As you show your dial, people will read the motto and quote it aloud. Your sundial is thus made more attractive than a dead piece of wood or stone; your personality is reflected in the motto. You can compose your own, or you can borrow one of the following expressions which have been written on sundials before. As you place one of these mottoes on your sundial, think how long ago some person was attracted by the verse as you are now. These mottoes go very far back in history and show that no matter how the way of living changes, human beings are practically the same; and so is eternal time!

1. I hold within my hand
   Grains of the Golden Sand
   How few, yet how they creep
   Through my fingers to the deep
   While I weep.—Edgar Allan Poe

2. I count only the sunny hours.
3. I am moved by light.
4. As a shadow, so is life.
5. To them that mourn the hours are slow
   But with the joyful swiftly go.
6. What is swifter than time?
7. I speak, but not to the blind.
8. It is later than you know.
9. Light guides me, the Shadow you.
10. Thou knowest my hour, not thy own.
11. God is my light, see His shadow.
12. I tarry not for the slow.
13. Tempus fugit.
14. Today dies tomorrow
    I wait for no man's lure.
15. Time and Tide wait for no man.
16. I'll return tomorrow.

In case you wish your sundial to be more accurate and marked so that it will show half- or quarter-hour divisions, it will be necessary for you to understand or have studied geometry. The following directions will show you how to do this.

ADVANCED ACTIVITY F.
GEOMETRY OF THE HORIZONTAL SUNDIAL

Materials. Drawing paper 12 by 18 inches; compass; protractor; ruler $\frac{1}{16}$-inch divisions; drawing pencil.

Directions.

1. Draw a square the size of the dial you want.
2. Divide this into four equal squares.
3. Label the lower rectangle *AOBCR* and *D* (see Fig. 40).
4. Draw *OR*, a double line, the thickness of the gnomon.
5. From *0*, draw a line *OM*, making angle *BOM* equal to 90 degrees minus the latitude.
6. Draw *OPM* equal to the same angle.
7. Lay off *PE* equal to distance *PM*.
8. Using *PE* as the base, mark off angles of 15 degrees to top line of square. Mark them I, II, III, IV.

★ 161 ★

9. For half-hour intervals, lay off angles of 7.5 degrees instead of 15 degrees.

10. For quarter-hour intervals lay off 3.75 degrees.

11. From 0, draw lines to I, II, III, etc.

12. Retain only the lines within the square.

13. The line AOB will become VI.

14. All intersecting hours to the right of the gnomon line (OP) will be P.M.

15. For A.M. hours, lay off measured distances to the left same as P.M. lines on the right, allowing for the thickness of the gnomon. These will be VI, VII, VIII, IX, X, and XI.

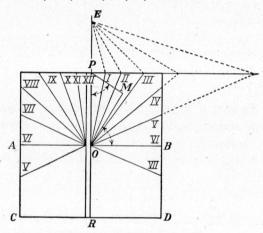

FIG. 40.—Geometry of sundial.

16. V A.M. and VII P.M. will be continuation of V P.M. and VII A.M. respectively (allowing for thickness of gnomon).

17. The gnomon need not be cut out in a perfect right triangle. It must have one angle at 0 along OP equal to the latitude of the location.

ADVANCED ACTIVITY G.
GEOMETRY OF THE VERTICAL SUNDIAL

Materials. Same as Activity F. (see page 161).
Directions.

1. Angle BOM is equal to latitude of the place instead of 90 degrees minus the latitude.

★ 162 ★

2. The gnomon angle is equal to the complement of the latitude instead of the actual angle.

STAR TIME

The astronomer finds his time by the stars, but his methods are too complicated to describe here. His clock shows star (sidereal) time, not sun time like the sundial, and not mean sun time like the ordinary clock. But you can tell time roughly by merely watching the Great Dipper (see page 20) and noting its position. Thus, you have a way of "tracking" time even during dark nights. The Dipper goes around the North Star once each night, just as the sun does. The Dipper gains a little each day on the sun. It goes back to the same place about 4 minutes earlier than on the night before. Therefore, it gains on the sun. Then each month we have to imagine the clock face turned 2 hours backward. So we must have a new clock each month or one with a movable dial. That is what we have in the star clock which you can make if you follow the directions below:

ACTIVITY H.   HOW TO MAKE A STAR CLOCK

Materials. One sheet of cardboard about 6 by 12 inches; one paper fastener (roundheaded); compass; scissors; knife; protractor; cardboard.

Directions.

1. Cut the cardboard into 2 pieces; a 6-inch square, and a disk 2½ inches in radius.

2. Cut a little "window" on the disk (see Fig. 41).

3. Draw the outlines of the Big Dipper.

4. On the disk, draw the skyline picture on the bottom, opposite to the window.

5. Using the compass on the square cardboard, draw circles having radii of 3, 2½, 2, 1¾, and 1½ inches.

6. Using the protractor, draw lines from the center point on the square 30 degrees apart.

7. Number these exactly as shown in Fig. 41.

8. Put in the months and dates exactly as shown in Fig. 41.

9. Make a small hole in the center of each piece of cardboard.

10. Push a roundheaded paper fastener through both disk and square. The disk should be on top and loose enough that you can turn it around.

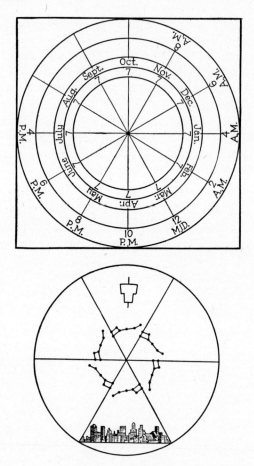

Fig. 41.—Star clock.

11. Turn the disk until the nearest date shows in the window.

12. On a clear night, face the north and hold the "clock" so that the "round head" is before you as the North Star is.

13. Turn the entire card until the horizon scene is at the bottom.

★ 164 ★

14. See which dipper diagram is like the real Dipper.

15. The line through the pointers of *that* diagram in a direction away from the North Star indicates the hour.

ADVANCED READING ACTIVITY

Jeans, Sir James: *Through Space and Time*. New York, The Macmillan Company, 1936.

Maynall, R. N., and M. L. Maynall: *Sundials*. Boston, Hale, Cushman and Flint, 1938.

Millikan, R. A., J. C. Merriam, H. Shapley, and J. H. Breasted: *Time and Its Mysteries*. New York, New York University Press, 1936.

Molesworth, Major F. C.: *The Military Uses of Astronomy*. London, Longmans, Green and Company, 1924. (Chapter XI.)

Wilson, P. W.: *The Romance of the Calendar*. New York, W. W. Norton Company, Inc., 1937.

World Almanac (astronomical section)—annual, or other similar almanac.

IX

You Can Make a Real Telescope

OWNING a telescope! What a dream! Perhaps you have yearned to have a real telescope of your own. It may be that you are one of the many boys and girls who like to watch the stars, have learned the constellations, and have seen all they can with the naked eye. Then you will want to see beyond that, especially if you have traveled to a distant observatory and waited in a crowded line for a few squints through a large telescope. It is fun to see the invisible craters on the moon, the dim rings around Saturn, and the marble-like moons racing around big, silvery Jupiter. If this makes you feel as if you want a telescope, do not think that you cannot have one; you can.

It is true that commercial telescopes are better than home-made ones, but they are also much more expensive. If you are handy with tools and like to experiment, you can make your own telescope. The cost of this can be kept within your pocket money. The most important cost is your "elbow grease" and perseverance. It will take you at least one month, but not more than four, to complete a telescope that you can actually use. You can build one in your school, camp, or club shops.

Of course, with this kind of telescope you will not be able to see the things that the big observatory telescopes show, but it will satisfy your wide-awake interest and curiosity.

Remember that the first tele- scope (see Frontispiece) used for astronomy by Galileo in 1610 was not a powerful instru- ment. Later on when Sir Isaac Newton made his first tele- scope, he showed what could be done in a simple way (see Fig. 42).

The best kind of homemade telescope is the reflector. This is a slightly curved mirror with a highly polished metal surface. The surface catches the star and

Fig. 42.—Newton's telescope.

planet light, and throws it forward, or reflects it to a point (the focus) where you can watch it. By placing an ordinary flat mirror diagonally at this point, the light can be reflected to the side where you can observe it more conveniently (see Fig. 43).

If you place a magnifying eyepiece at the side point, the image is enlarged so that you can see the planet or star perhaps 100 times bigger. Because the mirror is a great deal

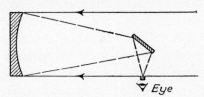

▽ Eye

Fig. 43.—Schematic diagram of reflecting telescope.

wider than your eye, it can catch that much more light. Since the fainter objects, like the moons of Jupiter and the rings of Saturn, are at such distances that they do not send enough light for your eye to see them, the large surface of

★ 167 ★

the curved mirror gathers the dim light and bunches it at one point.

A PREVIEW OF MAKING A REFLECTING TELESCOPE

The authors have heard many boys and girls comment on the difficulty of making a complicated-looking telescope. But the authors have also found out that as soon as these boys and girls understood the various steps in making a telescope, they went ahead with greater confidence. It may be that you need a little confidence. The motion-picture theaters show you a preview of future films so that you will have some idea of what the coming attractions are all about. In the same way, the following preview will give you a picture of what you have to do to make a reflecting telescope.

This type of telescope is made by rubbing together two flat glass plates, or disks, with water and some kind of abrasive between them. This rubbing makes a slight hollow or curve in the top disk and a hump on the bottom disk. The hollow disk becomes the reflecting mirror for the telescope and the humped disk is the tool which cuts the curve in the mirror. In order to make sure that the right kind of hollow or curve is being cut into the mirror, the cutting is started with a rough or coarse abrasive and finished with a fine abrasive. Then the curve in the mirror is tested to see whether it has been cut deep enough. This is done in a simple way by observing how the mirror reflects a flashlight beam when the flashlight is held at a certain distance in front of the mirror. This is called the "radius of curvature" test. It is used in order to make sure that the finished curved mirror will not reflect starlight and planet light so far ahead that the focus would be beyond a convenient distance for a frame or mounting.

When the radius of curvature test shows the focus to be about 50 or 60 inches (a convenient length for a beginner's telescope mounting), the curved disk is polished with opticians' rouge and water. The humped glass disk, which was used as the tool to cut the correct curve, is now used to polish the mirror. The humped tool is covered with a layer of melted rosin, and pressed into the curve of the mirror so that every spot on the mirror is touching the humped layer of rosin underneath it. A mixture of opticians' rouge and water is then spread (like the abrasives) between the glass disks and the mirror becomes smoothly polished. To test the mirror for this condition, another light test is made. This is known as the Ronchi test and is not as simple as the flashlight test. The Ronchi test shows whether the curved mirror is sufficiently smoothed as well as correctly curved. The mirror is ready to be covered with a layer of bright reflecting metal, such as silver or aluminum. Next, the mirror is securely fastened at one end of a suitable rigid frame or mounting. The magnifying eyepiece is fixed about 50 to 60 inches away from the mirror. Finally, the telescope is ready to bring the sky to your eye.

The following directions will guide you step by step so that you will not make any mistakes in constructing your telescope.*

The directions for making the telescope will be divided into the following sections:

A. *List of the Materials Needed.* You may obtain these materials as a complete kit from a commercial company, or you may buy the items separately.

B. *List of the Apparatus Which You Must Build.* You should build these before you start working on the telescope. The materials for the apparatus may be found around the home, camp, or school workshop.

C. *Procedure in Grinding the Mirror.* This will consist of numbered steps of directions which will tell you how to cut a curve into a glass disk by rubbing one glass disk upon another, using various grades of carborundum, emery, and

---

* These directions were summarized by Robert G. Cox, amateur telescope maker of New York City.

water as abrasives between the disks. The directions will also tell you of simple tests which you must follow to make sure that you are grinding the correct curve on the glass.

D. *Procedure in Polishing the Mirror.* These directions will tell you how to use rosin and opticians' rouge between the glass disks so that the one which is to become the telescope will be polished smoothly.

E. *Procedure in Testing the Curve of the Mirror.* These directions will give you the final test for determining whether the surface of the mirror is ready to be coated with silver or aluminum.

F. *Procedure in Mounting the Mirror.* These directions will tell you how you can mount the coated mirror and make it into a telescope.

A. LIST OF THE MATERIALS NEEDED

You may buy these from reliable companies advertising in the national science magazines. If you order a complete company kit, make sure that it includes the following materials. You can also order these items separately from the companies listed.

1. Two Pyrex glass disks (6 by 1 inch). About $2 apiece. Corning Glass Company, Corning, N.Y.
2. One pound No. 60 carborundum
3. One pound No. 100 carborundum
4. One pound No. 220 carborundum
5. One pound No. 400 carborundum

about 50 cents per pound

Carborundum Company of America, 601 West 26th St., New York, N.Y.

6. One pound No. 302 emery
7. One pound No. 303 emery
8. One pound No. 303½ emery

about 60 cents per pound

9. One pound opticians' rouge

American Optical Company, 70 West 40th St., New York, N. Y.

10. Two pounds of best grade rosin
11. One-quarter pound pure beeswax
12. One piece "channel" iron (1¼ by 12 inches)

13. One small, soft paint brush
14. One small magnifying glass (called linen counter)
    Local hardware store

B. LIST OF THE APPARATUS YOU MUST BUILD

I. *How to Make a Work Bench for the Telescope*

MATERIALS:

3 wooden cleats, 2 by ¾ by ⅝ inches (high)
1 wooden wedge, 4 inches long
Oil drum (100 gallons) empty, or
Old Victrola cabinet, or
Old ice box
Flat board 12 inches square, 1 inch thick

Any firm place which stands about waist-high is good enough for a telescope work bench. Some amateurs have used an empty oil drum filled with water. Others have filled a wooden barrel with bricks and old iron, or anything that has dead weight. If you can locate an old Victrola cabinet, saw off the legs even with the bottom; the top of the cabinet will be steady enough for grinding, while the record shelves can be used for storing the abrasives. Other telescope makers have converted old iceboxes into work benches. Use anything that is handy, firm, and steady and that has a flat top for securing the glass disk.

Fasten the 12-inch square flat board upon the top of the grinding stand. Draw a 6-inch circle in the center of this board. Screw two of the wooden cleats (2 by ¾ by ⅝ inches) on the edge of the circle about one-third the way around. Place one of the glass disks against these two cleats. Place the wooden wedge against the glass disk at an equal distance from the two cleats. Screw the third cleat tightly against the center of the wedge. With this arrangement, you should be able to push or pull the wedge and thus easily remove or fasten the disk. Remove the disk to a safe place. Spread two sheets of clean newspaper over the top of the work bench. Cut out the newspaper at the places where the wooden cleats can be felt under the paper. You are now ready for Procedure C, Grinding the Mirror.

II. *How to Make the Testing Stand for the Flashlight and Ronchi Tests*

MATERIALS:

2 boards, 12 inches square, 1 inch thick

2 right-angle irons, ½ inch wide
3 bureau drawer knobs about 2 inches in diameter
Flat wedge, 1 inch high, 8 inches long, 3 inches wide
2 10-penny nails
Adhesive tape

Fasten the two 12-inch square boards at right angles to each other with the angle brackets, putting the upright board about 4 inches away from the edge of the other board. The upright will be the front of the testing stand and will support the mirror. Draw a 6-inch circle at the center of the upright board. Drive the two 10-penny nails almost through the board. The nails should be on the bottom

FIG. 44.—Making the testing stand.

side of the circle about 4 inches away from one another. Wrap several layers of adhesive tape around the nails. The mirror will rest upon these padded nails, flat against the backboard. Fasten two of the bureau drawer knobs on the bottom of the front side near the edge. Fasten the other knob on the bottom at the center of the rear side (see Fig. 44). Slide the wooden wedge under the rear knob so that you can tilt the front end of the stand.

III. *How to Make the Wax Brush*

MATERIALS:
Piece of wood ⅛ inch thick, ⅞ inch wide, and over 6 inches long

★ 172 ★

Piece of cloth from clean hand towel, 4 inches long and 2¾ inches wide

Heavy twine

Fold the towel three times so that the width is divided equally. Put the piece of wood into the center of the folded towel and fold back the cloth over the wood. Leave a ¼-inch space between the towel and the bottom of the wood. Tie the cloth to the wood with heavy twine.

IV. *How to Make the Opticians' Rouge Mixture*

MATERIALS:

Small glass jar with a screw metallic cover

2 teaspoonfuls of opticians' rouge

Water

Punch one small hole in the cover of the jar. Put the rouge into the jar and add cold water to fill the jar three-quarters full. Shake for several minutes until the rouge is well mixed with the water. Whenever the directions call for rouge, shake the bottle thoroughly before you use it.

V. *How to Make the Light Slit and the Wire Edge for the Ronchi Test on Curvature*

MATERIALS:

1 foot of No. 20 bare copper wire

Brass plate 4 by 1 by ⅛ inches

Block of wood, 1 by 1 by 6 inches

Block of wood, 3 by 3 by ½ inches

1 piece flat glass, 2 by 2 by 1⁄16 inches

2 new double-edged razor blades

Tube of metallic cement

1 frosted 40-watt electric bulb

Tin can slightly larger than bulb

Electric extension cord and plug

1 bolt and wing nut, 1½ by ¼ inches

Drill a ¼-inch hole near one end of the wood block, 1 by 1 by 6 inches. Fasten the opposite end to the center of the block of wood, 3 by 3 by ½ inches. Drill a ¾-inch hole at one end of the brass plate and drill a ¼-inch hole at the opposite end of the plate. Cement a short piece (about 1 inch) of the No. 20 bare copper wire *directly over the center* of the ¾-inch hole. Using the wing nut and bolt, fasten the brass plate to the block of wood 1 by 1 by 6 inches.

Punch a hole 1 inch in diameter about the middle of the side of the can. Cement the piece of flat glass over this hole. Cement *one* of the double-edged blades to the glass; the cutting edge of the blade should be cemented vertically to the ground. Bring the other double-edged blade next to the cemented one so that their cutting edges touch. Pull the loose blade away very slightly, so there is a parallel slit between the blades. Cement the second blade to the glass. Mount the electric light bulb inside the can, using the extension cord and appropriate switches.

C. PROCEDURE IN GRINDING THE MIRROR

Before beginning to work with the actual directions, there are certain things and names which will be found throughout the

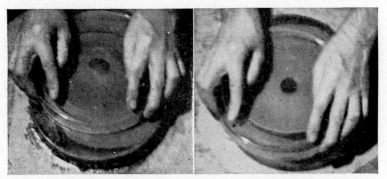

Fig. 45.—Explaining overhang and grinding stroke.

directions and which need explaining. Read these carefully and follow them *exactly*.

a. Whenever you read "wash" in the directions, it means to wash carefully and thoroughly *everything* with clean water. This washing will remove the larger abrasives which might scratch the glass mirror after it is smooth. Wash everything, that is, the mirror, the tool, and the bench top.

b. Wherever you read about the change of carborundum and emery from the rough to the fine numbers, you should *repeat* the *steps* taken with the *previous* grade of abrasive.

★ 174 ★

c. Wherever you read of 1¼-inch or ¼-inch grinding stroke, it means that you are to push the upper glass disk once forward and once backward over the lower disk. The number of inches means that the top glass disk is to be pushed forward and then stopped when it is 1¼ inches (or the required distance) over the edge of the lower glass disk. (This is called the "overhang.") The top glass disk is then pulled backward and stopped when the mirror is 1¼ inches (or the required distance) over the opposite edge of the lower disk. A stroke means a complete forward and backward motion of the top glass disk (Fig. 45).

1. Fasten one of the Pyrex disks to the top of the barrel with wooden cleats and a wedge (Fig. 46). This disk will be called the "tool," from now on. The other Pyrex glass disk will be known as the "mirror" from now on.

2. Wet the tool with water. Sprinkle ⅓ teaspoonful of No. 60 carborundum upon the wet tool.

3. Place the center of the mirror right upon the center of the tool (see Fig. 46).

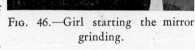

Fig. 46.—Girl starting the mirror grinding.

4. Press down slightly upon the mirror and make about one grinding stroke per second. Use the 1¼-inch overhang grinding stroke.

5. After you have made 10 to 20 grinding strokes, do two things:

    a. Take one short step around the barrel to the right (or left)

    b. Rotate the mirror slightly (about ¼ of a turn)

6. Every 10 to 20 strokes change your position around the barrel, one step at a time. When you feel the mirror move too smoothly, it is a sign that it is not cutting itself on the tool. Sprinkle more water and about ⅓ teaspoonful of the No. 60 carborundum on the tool and continue the grinding.

★ 175 ★

7. After you have been grinding for ½ hour, remove the wet mirror to the testing stand (see Fig. 47). Put the mirror on the stand with the ground side facing you. *Do not touch the wet surface.* It would be even better if you would wet the mirror with turpentine. The mirror is now ready for the first test, "the flashlight test"; this will roughly determine whether you have sufficiently curved the lens and are ready to change to a finer carborundum.

8. To make this test, unscrew the reflector from your flashlight. Hold the lighted flashlight against your left cheek on a level with your left eye. Move the flashlight from side to side and watch for the reflected light coming from the mirror (see Fig. 47).

Fig. 47.—How to make the flashlight test.

9. If the reflection moves in the same direction as the flashlight, walk slowly back from the mirror about 2 or 3 feet, watching the reflection as you do so. You should find a place where the mirror is completely covered with light. *Watch for this.* If you do not find this spot, walk a few feet backward or forward with the lighted flashlight until you reach the place where the reflection of the bulb on the mirror appears thousands of times larger and seems to cover the entire mirror.

10. To make sure that you have done everything correctly, check your movements with the following summary:

  I. *a.* Flashlight moved to right, image of bulb moved to right.

b. Flashlight moved to left, image moved to left. That is, the flashlight is inside the center of curvature.
II. You step slowly back a few feet:
    a. Flashlight moved to right, image moved to left.
    b. Flashlight moved to left, image moved to right. That is, the flashlight is outside the center of curvature.
III. You step slowly and very *slightly* forward:
    a. Image of bulb has disappeared and the whole mirror is covered with light.
    b. You cannot tell which way the reflected flashlight is moving. The mirror is completely covered with light even though the flashlight is moved *a very small* amount from side to side. That is, the flashlight is at the center of curvature.

11. At this point, you will not be able to tell whether the reflected light is going with or against the movement of the flashlight. Mark the spot where you are standing and measure the distance to the mirror. It should measure 128 inches. This point is the center of curvature of the mirror. It is equal to twice the focal length. (By allowing for further grinding and polishing, the focal length of your mirror will be 60 inches, which will fit a convenient mount.)

12. You must continue using the No. 60 carborundum, grinding until the distance from the flashlight to the mirror is 128 inches. Then wash *everything* clean of the No. 60 carborundum.

13. Wet the tool with clean water and sprinkle ¼ teaspoonful of No. 100 carborundum upon it. Change to a ½-inch overhang grinding stroke. Wet the tool and sprinkle more carborundum about eight times. After the fourth wetting, continue the grinding until it is very smooth.

14. With the small magnifying glass, examine the surface of the mirror. If you see large pits or holes, you must continue step No. 13 (about 3 more wettings should be sufficient) until the magnifying glass shows that the surface is even.

15. Wash both disks thoroughly with clean water and then dry them.

16. Draw pencil lines in all directions across the surfaces of the tool and the mirror. Put the dry mirror upon the dry tool. Take a few short (½-inch overhang) grinding strokes.

★ 177 ★

17. When all the pencil marks are "touched," or completely erased, the curve in the mirror is touching the hump of the tool at all points and you are ready for the next step. If you do not observe the pencil marks being affected, you must grind another wetting of No. 100 carborundum until you can observe this. Again wash everything with clean water.

18. Change to carborundum No. 220 for about one hour and examine the surface of the mirror with the magnifying lens for signs of uneven grinding. The pits and holes should be about the same size. Continue the grinding until this test shows even-sized holes on the mirror.

19. Again wash away all the abrasive with clean water. Change to carborundum No. 400. Do not forget to sprinkle water and carborundum upon the tool whenever the grinding gets too smooth. Keep on with this grinding until you can read large print through the wet mirror. Wash everything with clean water.

20. Carefully put $\frac{1}{4}$ teaspoonful of No. 302 emery in the center of the tool and add enough water to make a thick paste. Rub one finger over the tool. If your fingertip feels any small lumps in the paste, press down until they break, or remove the lumps if they will not break.

21. Carefully lower mirror upon tool. *Do not use any pressure.* The weight of the hands, resting lightly upon the mirror, is sufficient. Change to a short ($\frac{1}{4}$-inch) overhang grinding stroke until the surface of the mirror is smooth and free from pits as seen through the magnifying glass.

22. Repeat steps (No. 20 and 21), changing to emery No. 303 and emery No. 303$\frac{1}{2}$.

23. Carefully wash everything with clean water after emery 303$\frac{1}{2}$.

D. PROCEDURE IN POLISHING THE MIRROR

1. Melt the rosin in a small pot. Dip a clean spoon into the melted rosin and drop a bit into a tumbler of cold water until it is cooled and gummy.

2. Carefully press your teeth into the bit of rosin. If your teeth can make a small impression in the rosin, which then crumbles, it is ready for use.

3. If your teeth cannot make the rosin crumble, add a small amount of turpentine and stir.

4. If the rosin feels too soft under your teeth, heat until it is in the condition described in Step 2.

5. Put the tool and mirror into a pail of very hot water for several minutes. Remove the hot wet tool and dry it thoroughly, but leave the mirror in the water until later.

6. Make a collar of a piece of paper (20 by 1½ inches) around the tool and glue the loose end of the paper with a drop of hot rosin. Pour ¼-inch layer of the hot, prepared rosin over the tool, using the paper collar as a dam to stop the rosin from flowing off.

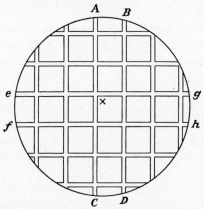

Fig. 48.—Waxed tool with rosin facing. *X* marks the center of the tool.

7. Allow the rosin to set until it does not squeeze in when you tightly press your finger against it. Tear off the paper collar from around the tool.

8. Dip your hands into soapsuds made of lukewarm water and cover the channel iron with a heavy layer of suds.

9. Press the channel iron into the soft rosin, slightly off-center making cuts in the rosin. First make cut *ABDC*. Then make the cut *EFGH*. The center of the tool must be at the corner of the center square of the cut rosin (see Fig. 48).

10. Using *BD* as one guide for the channel iron, make another cut into the rosin. Continue this cutting as in Step 10; that is, until the entire surface of the rosin is cut as shown in Fig. 48.

11. Make some hot water suds. Remove the mirror from the hot water (see Step 5). Cover the ground surface of the mirror with a heavy layer of the soap suds. *The soapy mirror is very slippery.* Cover

the surface of the rosin with hot water suds. Carefully hold the mirror and place it upon the rosin surface.

12. Press down heavily upon the mirror and use the short ($\frac{1}{2}$-inch) overhang grinding stroke.

13. Look down through the mirror to the cuts on the rosin. If you can see any uneven spots (that is, where the mirror does not touch the tool) continue the grinding stroke until the uneven spots disappear.

14. If the cuts on the rosin surface fill in as you grind, remove mirror to safe place and repeat pressing cuts with channel iron (Steps 9 and 10).

15. If the rosin gets so hard that you cannot make a change upon it, place the tool (rosin up) in very hot water until the rosin softens so that you can work it. However, change the overhang stroke to $1\frac{1}{2}$ inches.

16. Continue Steps 13, 14, and 15 until the cut rosin surface fits into the mirror without any uneven spots.

17. Remove the mirror from the tool and allow the tool to cool, then dry the tool.

18. While the tool is cooling, heat the beeswax in a small pot upon a stove or an electric heating unit until it is smoking hot.

Be careful that the wax does not catch on fire.

19. Dip the cloth wax brush (made in III, Procedure B) into the hot wax until it is filled with the melted wax. Quickly shake off the excess wax, but do not allow wax to get cold. Start at one end of one row of rosin squares and draw the brush *slowly* down the row. If the wax on the row is uneven or spotty, scrape off the wax and try again.

Never cover any square of waxed rosin with a second coat of wax.

Repeat the brushing with the hot wax until all the rosin squares are waxed.

As the wax cools quickly and gets too hard for working the next step, you should try to stay with the job until you are finished.

20. Put a heavy layer of hot soap suds upon the mirror. Place the mirror upon the waxed tool, then use the long ($1\frac{1}{4}$-inch overhang) grinding stroke which will make the mirror fit the waxed tool (see Step 16, Procedure C). If the mirror does not make a good fit with the tool, place the tool into warm (not hot) water. Repeat

Step 20 until there is a good fit. Then dip the tool into hot water for about two minutes.

21. Using the soft paint brush, put a thick coat of rouge upon the mirror.

22. Remove the tool from the hot water and clamp it tightly on the grinding stand.

23. Place the rouged mirror upon the warm tool. If you can see any air bubbles under the mirror, lift it slightly without permitting its surface to leave the surface of the waxed rosin. As you do this, move the mirror back and forth a few strokes.

24. When you have removed the air bubbles, fix the center of the mirror so that it is directly over the center of the tool. With the mirror in this position, place a weight of 20 to 40 pounds upon the mirror. Allow to rest for one-half hour.

25. Remove the heavy weight and use the short ($\frac{1}{4}$-inch overhang) grinding stroke. If the mirror jerks over the tool while you are using the stroke, go back to Step 24 and repeat the weight pressing. When the pressing is correct, you can push the mirror over the tool with a strong, but smooth "friction" and then the mirror is ready for the actual polishing with the rouge.

26. Using the short ($\frac{1}{4}$-inch overhang) grinding stroke, continue the rouge polishing for about a half hour. Watch through the mirror to see when the rouge mixture appears to be drying; then stop and brush some more rouge and water mixture upon the mirror. (Do not take too long to add the fresh, wet rouge.) Then remove and clean the mirror with water. Examine the polish on the curved surface. The polish should be clearer at the center than at the edge.

27. If the polish on the mirror is clearer at the edge or in between the edge and the center, you have made one of two mistakes:

   a. Your polishing tool did not make a good fit with the curve of the mirror.
   b. Your polishing-grinding stroke had an overhang greater than $\frac{1}{4}$ inch.

28. If the polish on the mirror is wrong, chip off all the hard dry rosin covering the tool and repeat all the work of Procedure D up to Step 26.

29. After you have made a new polishing tool and still there is no difference in the polish of the mirror, you must go back and

repeat all the work from Carborundum No. 220 (Step 18, Procedure B). If it is necessary for you to return to grinding with No. 220, then your pencil test was more than likely incorrect.

30. If your mirror is polishing correctly (from center to edges) continue the polishing for about 3 hours. Whenever it is necessary for you to stop working, wash and dry the mirror and clean off the working bench. When you are ready to continue the polishing, dip the tool into hot water, center the rouged mirror upon it, and press down with the heavy weights for about half an hour before you start.

31. To find out when the mirror is completely polished, use one of the following tests:

a. Focus the sun upon the polished surface near the edge of the mirror with the small magnifying glass. When the mirror surface has been polished sufficiently you will have difficulty seeing any image of the sun. If you can see the sun's image, you must continue the rouge polishing.

b. At night or when the sun is not visible, you may substitute a flashlight as a source of light. Unscrew the reflector from the flashlight and with the magnifying glass focus the light from the filament upon the edge of the polished surface of the mirror. Again you should have the same difficulty seeing the light image if the polishing is completed.

32. Your mirror is now ready for the final test for correct curvature.

E. PROCEDURE IN TESTING THE CURVE OF THE MIRROR

You have polished the mirror until it has passed the "image-edge" test (Step 31, Procedure D), but it may not be ready for the coating of aluminum or silver. Even though the surface of your mirror looks smooth to your eye and feels smooth to your finger, yet it may contain unevenness or irregularities which would ruin your telescope if you stopped working at this point. It will be necessary for you to note where these irregularities are and to do something to remove them. The Ronchi test is a sensitive light test which will reveal the presence and location of surface irregularities. Then directions will be given which will show you how to remove any irregularities and how to bring the surface of the mirror to its final polish. These directions will be similar to those in Procedure D (Polishing), only it will not be necessary to use any more rouge.

1. Place the mirror upon the padded nails of the testing stand.

2. Using the flashlight test of Steps 8 to 11, Procedure C, locate the center of curvature of the mirror. (It should be about 120 inches away from the mirror.)

3. At this point, place the light-slit and the wire edge (made in V, Procedure B). The height of the slit and wire edge and the point of the center of curvature should be *almost* the same. More than likely you will have to move the testing stand up and down with the wedge as well as forward and backward; that is, until the reflected flashlight beam comes to a focus right on the opening of the wire edge. This will take some patience and many trials.

4. With the center of curvature of the mirror on the same plane as the slit and wire edge, remove the flashlight and turn on the electric bulb inside the can. (CAUTION: The can soon becomes very hot and you really cannot work more than 5 minutes before you must put out the light for a few minutes to allow the can to cool.)

5. About 20 inches behind the wire edge, squint one eye and notice the image of the slit. Move head forward and observe the spot where the mirror is completely covered with the reflected slit of light. Slowly move the wire edge into the center of curvature of the reflected light. The wire will "cover" the entire mirror. Then move the wire edge *very slightly* forward. At this point, the mirror is examined for irregularities, and is known to be "inside the center of curvature."

6. Slowly move the wire edge so that you can see the reflection of the wire on the left side of the mirror. Then slowly move the wire edge from left to right, noticing the changing shape of the image of the wire.

7. If you have done everything as it should be done and have had more than the usual run of luck, your mirror will reflect the image of the wire as shown in Diagram (*a*), Fig. 49. The dark bands of the wire edge always remain the same, vertical, even, and straight. Your mirror is now *spherical* in shape and ready for the coating of aluminum or silver.

8. However, you will undoubtedly find some faults on the mirror surface because it is practically impossible to grind and polish a

perfect spherical mirror on first trial. The following are some of the common irregularities which your mirror might have:

Diagram (*b*), Fig. 49. As the wire edge is moved from left to right, your squinted eye sees the wire bands bent toward the center of the mirror, straight at the center and, as you continue moving the wire edge to the opposite side, the band reverses itself

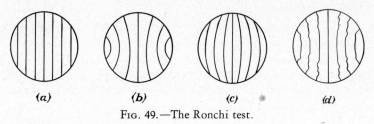

(*a*)   (*b*)   (*c*)   (*d*)

Fig. 49.—The Ronchi test.

but is still bent toward the center. This indicates a "hump" in the center of your mirror.

The remedy for this: Add water *only* to the rosin tool and cold press for a perfect fit which is absolutely necessary for a correct curve. Then use the 1- to 1½-inch overhang polishing stroke. As you polish, use the Ronchi test at frequent intervals. If, after 4 minutes of polishing, you cannot get the "spherical bands," lengthen the polishing stroke to 2 inches. Polish and test until the wire bands appear as they should.

Diagram (*c*), Fig. 49. As you move the wire edge from left to right, the image of the wire bands is bent away from the center of the mirror. This indicates that there is a hollow in the center of your mirror.

The remedy for this: Add water *only* to the rosin tool and cold press for a perfect fit. The hollow shows that there is a better fit at the center than at the edge. Then use a very short polishing stroke (⅛-inch overhang). Use the Ronchi test at frequent intervals in the polishing until the wire bands appear as they should.

Diagram (*d*), Fig. 49. If the wire bands are broken, zigzag, or very irregular, then there is a very poor fit between the mirror and the rosin tool. Be sure the center rosin square is *not* on the center of the tool.

The remedy for this: If the center rosin square is out of position, go back to the beginning of Procedure D (page 178) and repeat all the steps. However, do *not* use any more rouge; merely fix the rosin squares so that they make contact with the mirror at all points. Use the Ronchi test at frequent intervals, until the wire bands appear as they should. (You may change the forward and backward stroke to one slightly elliptical. This stroke will correct this irregularity better than the straight stroke.)

Your mirror is now ready to receive its metallic reflecting coating. You can do your own silvering by following the directions given in Letter Circular No. 32, United States Bureau of Standards, Government Printing Office, Washington, D. C. Silver, however, has not been found to be entirely satisfactory for an amateur's first telescope. It is recommended that you send your polished mirror to a firm that will put a coating of aluminum on it for a few dollars. The aluminum coating will last practically forever, while the silver wears off and must be renewed. (At the same time you send your mirror to be aluminized, you may include the flat piece of glass which is needed as a diagonal, as explained in the next section. The mirror and flat glass can be first covered with a heavy layer of absorbent cotton, packed with heavy cardboard or light wood, and then shipped parcel post.)

F. PROCEDURE IN MOUNTING THE MIRROR

The most important thing about the telescope mounting is that it must be strong and rigid; otherwise, as you are squinting at a star or planet, your fun is ruined because the sky object "jumps" out of focus and sight. Therefore, take pains to make a firm mounting so that the telescopic image will be steady and not wobble when someone walks near it. The second fact about the mounting is that it must be easily adjustable to swing and point to any part of the sky. If the mounting is to be portable, you must remember to make plans for ease of assembling.

The following directions are only tentative because it was felt that you would use your ingenuity and cleverness to adapt the mounting to the parts you may have on hand about the home, school, or club shop. The telescope mounting may be divided into sections: (1) the tube; (2) the axis. The tube is the frame which holds the mirror, the diagonal flat glass, and the eyepiece. The axis is the support or stand which holds the tube. It is capable of being

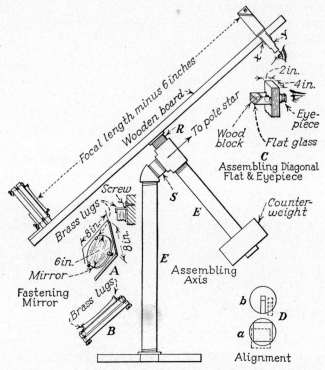

FIG. 50.—Mounting the telescope.

swung and pointed in two ways, up from the horizon to the zenith and completely around the horizon. You will need the following parts for each section of the mounting:

I. *The Tube* (*A, B, C,* Fig. 50)

MATERIALS:

 1 piece of wood, 2 by 4 by 2 inches longer than the focal length (about 60 to 68 inches) but not shorter than 57 inches

 2 pieces of heavy tin (about No. 20 gauge) 1½ by 6½ inches

1 piece of flat glass, 1½ by 2⅛ by ¼ inches. (If windshield glass is used, be sure it is not the shatterproof type.) This should be sent away to be aluminized (see page 185)
2 blocks of wood, 8 by 8 by 1 inch
2 right-angle brackets, ¼ inch wide
4 bolts and wing nuts, ¼ by 3½ inches
4 small springs (¾ inch long) to fit over bolts
1 piece of felt, 6 inches in diameter
1 bolt and nut, 1¾ by ⅛ inches
1 block of wood, 1½ by 1½ by 3 inches, cut in the following manner:

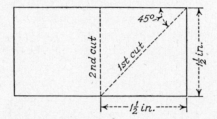

3 small pieces of brass, 1⁹⁄₁₆ inch long by ¼ inch wide by 1⁄16 inch thick
1 piece of brass tubing, 3½ inches long by 1¼ inch inside diameter (y in C, Fig. 50)
1 piece of brass tubing, 3½ inches long with an inside diameter large enough to allow brass tubing (y) to slide smoothly, yet firmly, through it
1 eyepiece (1-inch focal length) from school, group, or individual microscope*

II *The Axis* (E, Fig. 50)

MATERIALS:
2 pieces of wood, 2 by 4 by 28 inches
3 2-inch pipe flanges
2 2-inch pipe threaded nipples, 4 inches long
1 2-inch pipe T
1 2-inch 45-degree elbow
1 piece of 2-inch pipe, 2 feet long, with ends threaded

Odd heavy weights to use as counterweight, the amount to be determined by trial

1. Assemble the mirror as shown in Fig. 50.

    a. Diagrams *A* and *B* show how the mirror is securely fastened.

    b. Diagram *C* shows how the eyepiece and diagonal are attached to the long board by means of the 45-degree angle wooden block, the heavy tin, and two brass tubes. Brass tubing *x* should fit tightly in the hole and *must be perpendicular* to the board. The eyepiece is cemented to the outside end of tubing *y*. Brass tubing *y* should slide firmly yet smoothly inside brass tubing *x*.

    c. In the 45-degree angle wooden block ($1\frac{1}{2}$ inch square), drill a $\frac{3}{16}$-inch hole exactly $\frac{3}{4}$ inch from the right angle. Cement the flat diagonal mirror to the 45-degree angle side of this block, making sure that the aluminized side *faces* the telescope mirror.

    d. Diagram *D* contains two subdiagrams *a* and *b*, which you must use to be sure that the center of the mirror, the diagonal flat glass, and the eyepiece are in perfect alignment.

        (1) Assemble the mirror and flat, but *not* the eyepiece. Cover the mirror with a soft cloth. Look through the brass tubing *y*. The heavy lines in Diagram *a* are what you should see. If you see the square in the incorrect position of the dotted lines, you must adjust the position of the diagonal block of wood and bend the tin form until you can see the square just fit inside the circle.

        (2) Remove the cloth from over the mirror. Look through brass tubing *y* again. The heavy lines in diagram *b* are what you should see. If you see the incorrect outline as shown by the dotted lines, you must correct the position of the board controlling the mirror by loosening or tightening the wing nuts.

        (3) If you wish to check your alignment, fasten the eyepiece in position and focus the telescope on a star. Then defocus the eyepiece. If the alignment is correct, you should see the star as a disk with a black square in the center. If the black square is not in the center, loosen or tighten the wing nuts under the mirror until you do see this.

e. Diagram *E* shows one type of telescopic mount, using the pipe fittings listed in the materials for the axis. The base should be level and firm. The 45-degree elbow should be adjusted so that it makes an angle with the ground equal to the latitude of the location. You may adjust for this by fastening a wooden wedge under one side of the base flange, until the latitude angle is correct. A perpendicular line drawn through the center of the elbow and through the *T* should point directly to the Polar, or North, Star.

The center of the upper flange is fastened at the board's center of gravity. Fasten everything on the tube assembly and balance it on a chair. The point of balance is the center of gravity.

The counterweight can be determined only by trial. After you have determined how much weight is needed to counterbalance the tube assembly, you can fill the counterweight pipe with the proper amount of melted lead.

To permit the telescope to swing and point to any part of the sky, allow some play in the threads of the nipples at *R* and *S* in Fig. 50.

The authors strongly urge you to experiment with the mounting and to read the more advanced books and magazine articles listed below for further ideas. The subject of mounting is too large to be adequately treated in a few pages. For further help it would be wise for you to contact one of the amateur telescope-making groups, names and schedules of which appear each month in *Sky and Telescope* and *Popular Astronomy* magazines.

ADVANCED READING ACTIVITY

Bell, Louis: *The Telescope*. New York, McGraw-Hill Book Company, Inc., 1922.

Dimitroff, George Z., and Baker, James G.: *Telescopes and Accessories*. Philadelphia, The Blakiston Company, 1945.

Ingalls, Albert: *Amateur Telescope Making*. New York, Scientific American Publishing Company, 1935.

Ingalls, Albert: *Amateur Telescope Making—Advanced*. New York, Scientific American Publishing Company, 1937.

Pendray, Edward G.: *Men, Mirrors and Stars*. New York, Funk and Wagnalls Company, 1935.

Scientific American (monthly). Section on telescope making.

X

Squinting through the
Magic Eye of the Telescope

ON A clear night, the sky sparkles with silver dots, twinkling and shining like diamonds. Sometimes the moon appears among the stars like a great golden disk. Many of us look at these interesting and beautiful sky objects and wonder how they would look if we could visit them. Perhaps we never shall. But we can bring them down to earth and look at them close at hand. Set up your telescope on the school roof, in the schoolyard, at your camp, or any place where you can get an unobstructed view of the sky. Maybe you have made a reflecting telescope or own a spy glass. Your school, scout group, or camp, however, may have a telescope.

A telescope has two purposes. It is a magnifying glass for the close-up objects like the moon or planets and makes them appear larger just as though we were close to them. But it has another purpose. It acts like a funnel, gathering light and focusing it into our eyes so that we can see objects so dim that to our naked eye they are invisible. That is what we mean by bringing the sky down to earth.

In Chapter II each constellation is described and a list of interesting telescopic objects to look at is given. Here we will describe briefly the various kinds of things there are so that you will have a list of spots in the sky where you can find objects being studied by great observatories all over the world.

MOON

To BEGIN close at home, we turn our attention to our own moon. This bright object in the sky appears large to us but it is one of the most insignificant astronomical bodies. It is only 2,160 miles in diameter. It would require more than 50 moons to build our earth. It swings around the earth in the same kind of a path that the earth follows around the sun— only much smaller. The sun is about 93,000,000 miles away from the earth but the moon is only about 240,000 miles from us. While the earth requires a whole year to go around its path, the moon takes only a month to complete its circuit around us. In fact that is what the word month means— "moonth."

Your glimpse at the moon will reveal it to be a giant ball of rock, rough and rugged, very much like the Bad Lands of the West, only more so (see Fig. 51). Unless the moon is full, which is the worst time to study it in a telescope, some of it will be in shadow. Suppose we begin at the beginning.

Just after sunset some evening you will see a crescent moon low in the west. It is thin and silvery. For the past several days no moon was visible in the sky, so it is no wonder that the ancient watchers of the sky called this a "new moon," and really thought it was. If you look carefully either with or without the telescope you can see the rest of the big disk faintly lighted by reflected "earthshine." This is known as the " old moon in the new moon's arms."

For the next week or ten days the moon offers its best view in the telescope. As the thin crescent widens, the "terminator," that is, the line between the day and night on the moon, moves across the disk and reveals new wonders. Even with a small instrument we can see **many** interesting lunar sights.

Even upon your very first look at the moon, you will notice that its surface has light and dark spots scattered over it. These dark places look very much like great bodies of water and back in 1610 Galileo thought they were. He called them "seas," *maria* in Latin, and even today they are known

Fig. 51.—As the moon looks through the great telescope at Mt. Wilson Observatory.

by that name all over the world. Galileo, you know (see Frontispiece), was the first person to turn a telescope to any heavenly body, and the moon was the first thing he gazed upon with his new instrument that was probably not so good as yours. We know now that the moon has no air nor any water on its surface, but Galileo had no way of finding this out.

★ 192 ★

Looking more carefully, you can see many large rings on the surface. These are the "lunar craters." They may have come from volcanoes or from the fall of meteorites when the moon was soft and plastic. Some of these great ringed plains are more than 100 miles in diameter, much larger than any crater on the earth. Some of the mountains are in ranges and bear the same names as the ranges on the earth. Night after night you can explore this barren waste and see nothing but a dead world, burning hot under a blazing sun and freezing cold in the dark places, with no plants, no animals, no life of any kind.

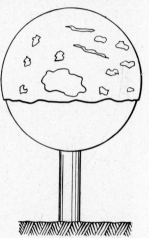

FIG. 52.—Model of moon.

ACTIVITY: MOON MAKING

Materials. Modeling clay; croquet or small bowling ball, 3 inches or larger in diameter; pointed piece of wood, shape and size of a pencil; telescope or field glass; pointed broomstick about 3 feet in length with finishing nail driven in top.

Directions.

1. Press out the clay so that it forms a flat mat, $\frac{1}{8}$ to $\frac{1}{4}$ inch and about 8 inches square.

2. Hammer the ball against the finishing nail on top of the broomstick.

3. Wrap the clay mat around the ball so that the clay becomes smooth and round like a ball.

4. Trim the clay mat into a hemisphere of the diameter of the ball. Do not remove (see Fig. 52).

5. When you are observing through the telescope or field glass, take this with you. Set it up near the telescope by gently shoving it into the ground.

6. Look at the moon through your instrument. Pick out the prominent "seas," large craters, and long mountain ranges.

7. Try to estimate their location on the moon by thinking of its surface as the face of a clock. Thus a crater in the upper right-hand section of the moon could be placed at 1 or 2 o'clock.

Chart of the Moon

CHART 4.

8. Using the "hour clock and edge distance" for determining the different places on the moon, make dents and ridges on the clay to represent these objects.

9. When you have finished, remove the moon model and place it on exhibition in your science room, hobby corner, or merit badge display.

PLANETS

SOME of the neighbor worlds are suitable for studying with a small telescope. Some of them are so far away that they do not present interesting sights for us. The ones we shall study are Venus, Mars, Jupiter, and Saturn. The others, we know by experience, are not exciting enough to be worth studying and they are so difficult to find in the sky that you will be disappointed if you attempt to find them. For the planet's constellation position, see page 131.

VENUS

THIS planet is very much like the earth; about the same size and not very different in its distance from the sun. While we speak familiarly about Venus, we have never

FIG. 53.—Venus looks like our moon. (*Yerkes Observatory Photograph.*)

★ 195 ★

really seen the planet! We see only the dense cloudy atmosphere around it. It was Galileo who first observed something that you can easily see. He noticed that Venus presents phases just like the moon and announced to the world that "Venus looks like the moon." When you observe this for the first time you will be as astonished as Galileo himself was many years ago (see Fig. 53).

MARS

THIS planet is the one that people are most interested in. It is about half the diameter of the earth and about half again as far from the sun. Its year is about twice as long as

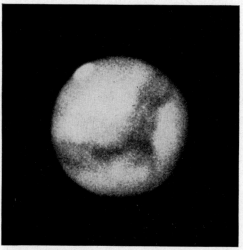

FIG. 54.—Mars and its markings. (*Yerkes Observatory Photograph.*)

ours, but the day on Mars is nearly the same length. Through a small telescope one can see the white caps on the poles of the planet. These are no doubt made of snow and ice just like the polar caps on the world. Sometimes we can see the South Pole cap and at other times, the North. These are best seen when we are close to Mars. If the "seeing" is good, you may be able to notice a dark mark near the equator of

★ 196 ★

Mars. The main color of the planet is red. This dark spot may be vegetation. It changes in size as the seasons on Mars change. Fantastic stories are written about the Man from Mars. Unfortunately, even with the largest telescopes, no inhabitants could be seen, not even things as large as cities. So the astronomer cannot say whether this neighbor world of ours is or is not inhabited (see Fig. 54).

JUPITER

ONE of the first sights that Galileo caught in his new toy—the telescope—was Jupiter and its four moons. Galileo called these moons the "Medicean planets" after the money backer of his telescope study. Jupiter is the largest of the

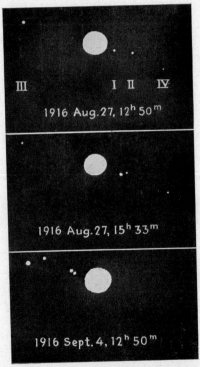

Fig. 55.—Jupiter and its moons. (*Yerkes Observatory Photograph.*)

★ 197 ★

sun's family. It has a diameter 11 times that of the earth's. As you know, the earth is flattened at the poles about 27 miles. But this giant is so much flattened that you can see it in the telescope. This is because the planet spins so rapidly. Its day is about 10 hours, less than half as long as our own day. The year, however, is about as long as 11 of ours. It has nine moons but only four can be seen in an ordinary telescope. These four tiny points of light look like stars (and Galileo first thought they were). Sometimes we can see two on each side and at other times three on one side and one on the other. In fact, we are likely to find them in most any position. Sometimes one or more seems to be missing. Then it is either in front of or behind the planet. These moons are so lively in their journeys around the big planet that it is lots of fun to watch them night after night and to see them always in different places. Someone once said that it looked like a "basket ball with marbles around it." As you will see the planet itself has dark lines crossing it (see Fig. 55).

SATURN

THIS is no doubt the most beautiful single object that comes to us through the telescope. It is almost as big as Jupiter and has nine moons (only one of which we can easily see), but in addition, it is surrounded by a beautiful ring

FIG. 56.—Saturn and its ring. (*Yerkes Observatory Photograph.*)

system. This ring is wide and flat and so thin that when we see it edge-on it really disappears except in the very largest instruments. The ring is made up not of solid material like cardboard, but of millions and millions of tiny moons so close together that to us they look solid (see Fig. 56).

NEBULAE

THESE great masses of glowing gas are difficult to see. The great observatories photograph them with long exposures and the pictures show details that no eye can see with a telescope. Among the descriptions in Chapter II are a number of these objects and when you look for them in the sky, they will appear merely as small cloudy spots. With your eyes wide open and your imagination afire, you can picture to yourself, as the astronomer does, the wonder expressed in these dim and distant objects (pages 21, 39, 67, 79).

CLUSTERS

THESE objects are really of two kinds, one called "open" clusters and the other, "globular" clusters. The open clusters are nothing more than groups of stars rather widely separated and having a common motion through the sky (see pages 29, 55). The globular kinds are more like swarms of bees, thousands of stars seeming to be packed tightly together. Actually they are not, but because they are so distant this appearance is likely to fool us. In small instruments these clusters look very much like nebulae and many years ago before the better telescopes were built, many were mistaken for such. The Pleiades (see page 49) is an open cluster. In Hercules (see page 59) you can see the best globular cluster.

SPIRAL NEBULAE

THESE objects are great universes of stars that are very distant from us. They cannot be of much interest to those having small telescopes. The one mentioned in Andromeda (see page 71) is the best.

★ 199 ★

THE MILKY WAY

THIS belt around the sky is mentioned in a number of the constellations. Here you can find many beautiful star fields for your telescope, even more than are mentioned by name. This is the place where you as an amateur astronomer can do your own exploring and discovering (see pages 25, 65).

DOUBLE STARS

THESE offer a great deal of material for study. When you see two stars very close together they may actually be close, that is, two suns in the same solar system. Or they may be merely in line, like two lamps that you see along the road and not actually near together.

ADVANCED READING ACTIVITY

Fath, F. A.: *Through the Telescope*. New York, Whittlesey House, McGraw-Hill Book Company, Inc., 1936.

McKready, Kelvin: *A Beginner's Star Book*. New York, G. P. Putnam's Sons, 1937.

Norton, A. P.: *Star Atlas*. London, Gall and Ingalls, 1937.

Olcott, W. T.: *Field Book of the Skies*. New York, G. P. Putnam's Sons, 1914.

Schurig-Götz: *Himmels-Atlas*. Leipzig (Germany): Ed. Gaeblers Geographisches Institut, 1933.

XI

Space Views

Pictures are a great help to us in studying the sky, especially if we do not have a telescope. Even the objects in the sky look "flat" but most of them are not. If we could add the third dimension a lot of things would be clearer. We can do this if we use a stereopticon. For this, we must have pictures taken specially for this use and a viewer for them.

The moon looks like a plate or disk, yet it is a great ball of rock. Through a large telescope you gain this feeling of roundness. The stars are not all the same distance away but they look as though they are. Even what we call a constellation and think of as a group of stars may not be. We are so far away and have so little chance to feel these differences in distance that we lose sight of this fact. The planets all go around the sun in paths that are almost circles but these circles are tilted at various angles. That is hard to show in pictures. Even a drawing in a book does not show it clearly. The way the earth swings around a great spiral, like a corkscrew, is hard to imagine but easy to see if we can get far enough away. Many people cannot understand why we do not have an eclipse of the sun every month. If you could see the tracks of the earth and moon, you would know. Then there are meteors and comets—well, look at the pictures.

It is to answer some of these questions and to give you a clear picture of how the various parts of our great universe are put together that the authors have made up this section. So far as we know this is the only book in which pictures of the heavenly bodies are shown in this way.

On the following pages are many stereopticon pictures with a description for each one, telling what to look for and explaining what you will see. Since the pages of this book cannot be torn out for a regular stereopticon, you will have to build your own special one. This will fit over the "stereo" pictures in the book where you can see the "other side of space" right in your classroom, den at home, or library at camp.

ACTIVITY A. HOW TO MAKE A "STEREO" VIEWER

Materials. Sheet of cardboard about 18 by 12 inches; 2 magnifying glasses about 1½ inches in diameter (price, 10 cents each); gummed paper; ruler; scissors; and compass.

Directions.

1. Look through the magnifying glass on a picture or printed page in a book. Move the glass up and down until you can see clear and sharp.

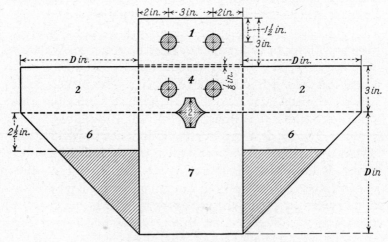

Fig. 57.—Drawing of stereo viewer.

★ 202 ★

2. Measure the distance between the glass and the book. (This will give D in Fig. 57.)

3. Repeat this with the other glass.

4. If one glass is 5 inches away and the other $5\frac{1}{2}$ inches; make an average and call the distance D, $5\frac{1}{4}$ inches.

5. On the cardboard, measure off the distances from the following drawing (see Fig. 57).

6. *Be sure to make D equal to the number of inches at which you saw most clearly through the lenses.*

7. Cut the cardboard on the heavy full lines.

8. Fold the cardboard on the dotted lines.

9. Throw away the cardboard from the shaded parts.

10. Fold (1) under (4) and "sandwich" the lenses between them.

11. *Move the lenses around until they are centered exactly in the round holes.*

12. Fasten (1) and (4) and lenses with the gummed paper.

13. The lenses should make a *tight* fit.

14. Fold down (2), (6), and (7) and fasten with gummed paper.

15. Fasten the edge of another card the size of (2) between the lens opening to separate the lines of sight. This is not necessary but will make the pictures clearer.

Fig. 58.—Using stereo viewer.

ACTIVITY B.
LOOKING THROUGH THE "STEREO" VIEWER

Materials. Stereopticon made from above directions.

Directions.

1. Select a place where there is a good, strong light.

2. Place the book on a steady table. Have the picture side of the page toward you.

3. Make sure the light hits the picture.

4. Place the viewer *exactly* on the lines at the bottom and the side of the page.

5. Look through the lenses (see Fig. 58).

ADVANCED READING ACTIVITY

De Sitter, W.: *Cosmos*. Cambridge, Harvard University Press, 1932.

Jeans, Sir James: *The Universe around Us*. New York, The Macmillan Company, 1934.

Proctor, Mary: *The Romance of the Comets*. New York, Harper & Brothers, 1929.

Proctor, Mary: *The Romance of the Sun*. New York, Harper & Brothers, 1927.

THE GREAT DIPPER THROUGH THE EYES OF A GIANT

★

WHEN we look up toward the North Pole of the sky we see the eight stars that to us form the Great Dipper. If we were closer to these stars and had eyes that were not 3 inches apart but millions of miles apart these eight stars would not look so much like a dipper. The space view gives us such an opportunity. At the bend of the handle, Mizar and Alcor seem to us close together, but Alcor is much nearer to us than Mizar. They are in the same direction from us but about 30 trillion miles apart. Notice the other stars, some near, others far away. All over the sky the stars look the same distance from us, but some are neighbors while others are so far away the light takes hundreds of years to travel to us.

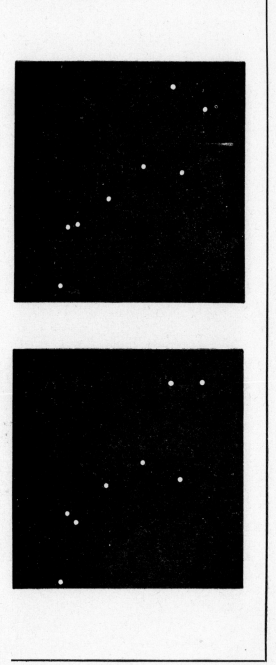

M ANY will recognize this Yerkes Observatory space picture as the constellation Orion (see page 78). The three belt stars and Rigel show plainly. Near the bottom of the picture is a meteor track starting from the star Saiph (see page 89). Meteors are tiny dust particles flying through space; they glow and sparkle when they fly into our atmosphere. The friction of the air burns them up.

Near the top is another trail drawn on the picture to show how a "shooting star" that is really going away from us (look through the viewer) appears to flash across the sky in front of you (look without the viewer).

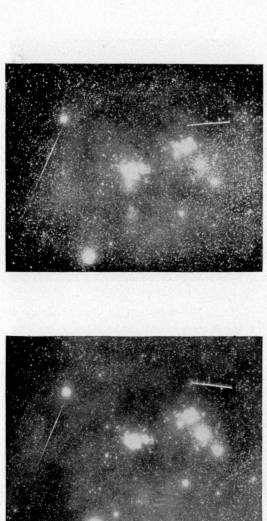

A STAR CLUSTER

★

THIS space picture made at the Yerkes Observatory shows how the stars in a cluster like the one in Hercules would look if we were close to it. The stars are so far away that we cannot take space photographs of them but we can make pictures that look like space photographs. These clusters are called "globular" because the stars are "globed" together like a swarm of bees flying through the air. Some are much closer to us than others. Some are in the center of the swarm while others are on the edges.

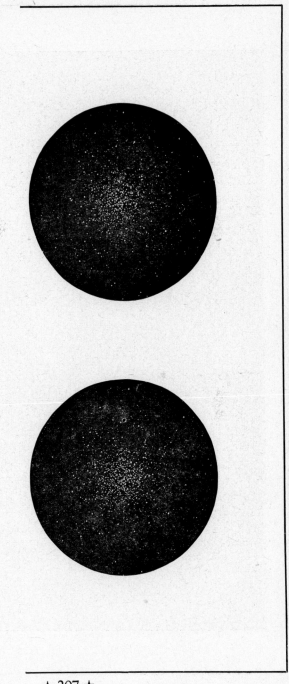

★

THIS Yerkes Observatory picture of the moon shows that it is a great ball of rock. The markings we see making the "man in the moon" and so on are great smooth dark spots. Around one of the craters near the top are lines running out in all directions making it look like a peeled orange. Moonlight is sunlight reflected back to us. Half of the moon is always lit by sunlight, just as the earth is half in light and half in darkness. There is no atmosphere on the moon, no clouds, no rain to change our view of this near neighbor.

MOREHOUSE'S COMET (OCTOBER 15, 1908)

★

STARS, planets, and other objects in the sky are all so far away that they seem to our eyes to be all at the same distance. They are not, however. The nearest star is 277,000 times as far away as the sun, yet they both seem to be the same distance. Comets come very close to the earth sometimes, but they still look as far away as the stars. This space picture shows us how close the comet is and how far away the stars are. It was made at the Yerkes Observatory on October 15, 1908. The stars are tiny streaks because the comet was moving rapidly across the sky and the camera followed the comet.

★

HERE we see this great comet as it appeared at the Yerkes Observatory on November 16, 1908. Comets move around the sun in orbits like the earth's (see page 123) except that they are long and narrow, like a rubber band lying on a table. Notice the delicate formations in the comet's tail, and how the stars shine right through it undimmed. A comet's tail is composed of gas and other light substances and it shines mostly by sunlight reflected from it. The filmy tails of comets are millions of miles long.

MOON NEARING THIRD QUARTER

★

To our unaided eyes, the moon looks like a flat disk—many people say "as large as a dinner plate." But a dinner plate looks large if we hold it close to our eyes and small if it is far away. So you cannot measure size that way! Through a telescope the globe shape of the moon becomes plainer and then we see that the dark spots are smooth. Galileo thought they were oceans or bodies of water. Better telescopes showed that this was not true and on this space picture you can see the round craters in the seas. Yerkes Observatory.

★

THE sun is a great globe of glowing gas, 864,000 miles in diameter. On its bright surface frequently appear spots. Sometimes they can be seen without a telescope, but that does not often happen. These spots are thousands of miles across. We do not know much about them, but astronomers believe that they are great tornadoes in the sun's atmosphere and that they send us high-power electrical charges that make the northern lights. There are two groups of spots on this Yerkes Observatory photograph. Can you see them? Never look directly at the sun without using a dark glass because the strong sunlight will burn your eyes.

SATURN AND THE MOON

★

THE moon is so much closer to us than the planet Saturn that in this space picture we can see it standing out in space with Saturn behind it. When the moon is new in the western sky after sunset it is a thin crescent. For a few days, while the crescent is thin, we can see the rest of the moon's surface faintly lit up with a pale light. That is sunlight reflected from the "day side" of the earth shining back to the moon and is therefore called "earth shine." In this picture from the Yerkes Observatory the moon is about a quarter million (250,000) miles away, while Saturn is nearly a billion (1,000,000,000) miles from us.

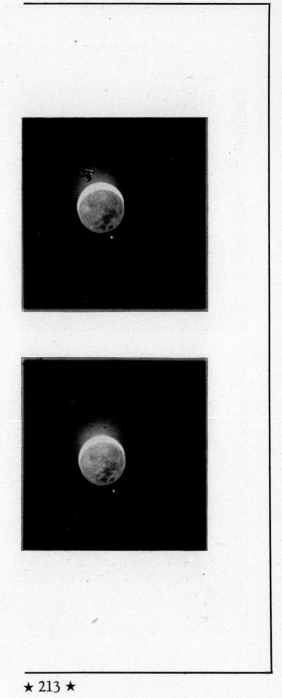

★

SOME DAY on Mt. Palomar, Calif., this reflecting telescope will be photographing the stars. In this picture you see a celluloid model in its exact proportions. The disk at the bottom of the barrel-shaped portion is the glass mirror nearly 17 feet across. The operator sits up at the top of this barrel in that little tube pointing upward. He presses buttons that control motors moving the instrument, which weighs several hundred tons. California Institute of Technology—Model by Westinghouse.

A COMET'S PATH AROUND THE SUN

★

COMETS travel around the sun in orbits just as the planets do. The planets' paths are nearly circles and all of them lie nearly in the same direction, like a lot of rings lying on a table. But comets cut through these planet paths in all sorts of directions. This picture shows the earth and its path around the sun. A comet speeds by from above the earth's path to below it, all the while keeping its tail turned away from the sun. This motion of the comet and its tail is difficult to see by watching a comet in the sky.

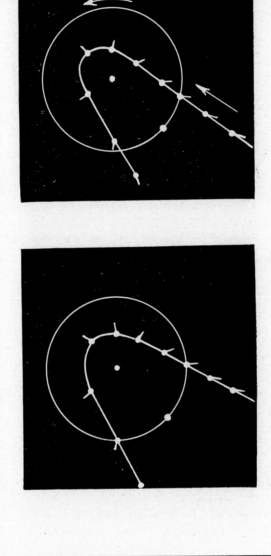

★

ON CERTAIN nights of the year a careful study of the meteors or shooting stars will show that they appear to be coming from some particular part of the sky, some constellation. Actually they are coming at us in parallel lines, but just as the railroad tracks, always the same distance apart, seem to meet way off, these trails appear to come from their radiant. This space view shows how meteors look to us (without the viewer) and how they actually are (with the viewer). Every so often though a stray meteor may look as though it is coming from the radiant, but really is not. Can you find one of these on this space view? We are sure you cannot without the viewer.

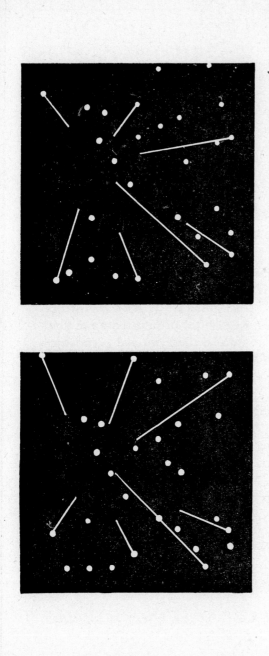

XII

Photo-trailing the Stars

TRAILING the stars and planets in the night sky with a camera offers you as much challenge and enjoyment as the taking of animal and plant pictures. If you ever thrilled at photographing the nesting of birds or in catching in your lens the colorful design of snakes, then you had better keep your camera open after sundown and make a record of Nature's calendar as shown by the stars in the night sky.

Trail pictures of the brilliant constellations, of the evening planets, of unexpected meteor flashes and the many faces of the silvery moon will give you worth-while additions for your album of nature shots. Your favorite camera—it may be a simple box camera or an f 6.3 or a complicated 35 mm.— loaded with fast film and fastened to a tripod stand or a home-made camera holder are the only equipment you will need for nearly all sky shots, with the exception of the moon; for this picture you should fasten your camera to a telescope. The telescope need not be large or expensive. The picture of the moon (see Fig. 59) was taken through a telescope such as the manufacturers advertise in scientific and craft magazines.

In photographing the stars you can expect to use much

longer exposures than the usual split-second snapshots. An exposure meter would tell you that the amount of light reaching the earth from these night objects is ridiculously small. However, by extending the time of exposure to several seconds or even to several hours, the film can react to this cumulative

Fig. 59.—The moon. (*Photograph by Harry Goff, Astronomy Club, Smedley Junior High School, Chester, Pa.*)

light and build up an impression of lines of light. You must remember that the camera is moving with the earth from west to east. Therefore, the stars will seem to move in the opposite direction, causing lines of light on the film. These lines are called "star trails." These trail lines will vary in

★ 218 ★

width according to the distance of the sky objects. The trail of Venus, for example, appears immense in comparison to that of Jupiter or Saturn or the distant giant stars because Venus is much closer and so leaves a wider light trail.

A careful study of your star-trail album pictures will show you many of the fundamental facts of astronomy: the magnitude of the stars and planets as related to distances from the earth, the diurnal and annual motion of the celestial sphere, the shifting in altitude of the ecliptic, the apparent parabolic journeys of Venus and Mercury, the retrogression of Mars, Jupiter, and Saturn, the relation of the position of the Big Dipper to the season of the year and to the time of the night, the circumpolar motion of certain constellations, the relation of altitude of sky objects to navigation—all these are but a few facts of elementary star study which your star-trail pictures will simplify for you.

CAMERA TECHNIQUES

1. Pick a good location, preferably a high point away from bright city lights and heavy truck traffic.

2. Enhance the composition of the picture by choosing a background of trees or a hillside.

3. Use fast film or plate.

4. Prop the camera firmly and rigidly.

5. With a magnifying glass focus the camera on the constellation in question, keeping it centered.

6. Open the aperture as wide as possible; with fast lenses, for better definition, the stop can be reduced in half.

7. If you can feel dew collecting on any metal object, you can be sure there is dew on the camera; carefully wipe this off the lens without moving the camera. You may have to do this several times during a 2- or 3-hour exposure.

8. If your film is "sent out," ask the finisher to develop it for contrast and to print all negatives, even those which appear to contain no picture.

9. Be prepared to experiment and do not let a few early failures cause you to stop your star trailing.

SUGGESTED LIST OF SKY PICTURES

A. Circumpolar Constellations (see pages 20 to 25 and Fig. 60).

    1. Focus center of finder on the Pole Star (see page 22).

    2. Open shutter for two hours; avoid longer exposures which make overlapping trails.

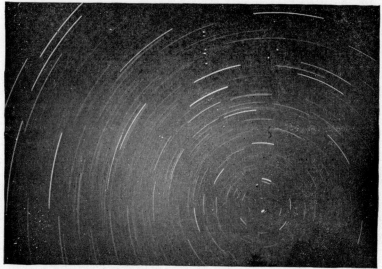

FIG. 60.—Circumpolar Star Trails. (*Photo by* **G. W.** *Sweet.*)

    3. Remember that these groups revolve counterclockwise about 15 degrees an hour around the North Star (see star clock on page 164).

    4. To obtain the configuration of the constellation on your printed copy, draw light dotted pencil lines connecting the individual stars; guide yourself by referring to the star charts in Chapter II.

B. Planets on the Zodiac or Ecliptic

    1. Consult tables, pages 132 to 135, for the constellation position of Venus, Mars, Jupiter, and Saturn in the month of the year you are taking the picture (see Fig. 61).

    2. When two or more planets appear in the same constellation, they are said to be in conjunction. (See Fig. 62.) Focus the

camera on the constellation in question, keeping the planets in the center of the finder.

3. Take two pictures, one with a 4-second exposure, the next with a 2- to 3-hour exposure.

4. Repeat the longer exposure picture at different intervals for several months.

Fig. 61.—Planet Jupiter in Constellation Leo. (*Photograph by G. W. Sweet.*)

5. You will have to enlarge the short (four-second) exposure because the planet image will be very small.

6. Compare the several long exposure prints. Notice that the star trails are fixed, while those of the planets, especially Mars and Venus, have moved in relation to the stars in the group.

C. Meteor Trails

1. Consult Table IV, page 94, for the meteor calendar for the best dates of the year to catch a picture of these elusive wanderers from space.

2. The procedure for taking meteor trails is the same as for taking star trails.

3. Plan to expend some film on this interesting but uncertain venture.

★ 221 ★

FIG. 62.—Conjunction of the planets, Venus, Mars, Jupiter, and Saturn, May, 1940. Bottom trails were made by an automobile and express trains. f 6.3, super-pan. (*Photograph by Joseph M. Joseph.*)

★ 222 ★

While the chances are not great that you will catch a meteor flash bright enough to affect the film (see page 206 and Fig. 63), it is worth the effort and a film or two. If you should be lucky enough to have your wide-open camera pointing to the spot in the sky where a meteor is exploding (a bolide, see page 90) with the brilliancy

Fig. 63.—Perseid Meteor near Vega. (*Photograph by James H. Logan of Texas Observers. Courtesy of Sky and Telescope.*)

of a magnesium flare, you would be one of the few amateurs to have this rare picture in your album.

ADVANCED READING ACTIVITY

Bernhard, H. J., Dorothy Bennett, and H. S. Rice: *New Handbook of the Heavens.* New York, Whittlesey House, McGraw-Hill Book Company, Inc., 1941.

King, E. S.: *A Manual of Celestial Photography*, Boston, Eastern Science Supply Company, 1931.

★ XIII ★

Truth Trailers

Down through the ages, man has been studying nature to learn the truth. The story of astronomy is the search for this truth. We never know the truth and perhaps never will, but we get little bits of it here and there and try to put them together to make a complete picture of nature. It is like a puzzle of many pieces. Sometimes we fit in the right piece and then we find one that will not seem to fit in anywhere. If we keep it where we can find it, we will be able to fit it in somewhere. Sometimes we fit in a wrong piece and have to take it out to make the right one fit. This is the way astronomy has developed. Some of the facts the early observers found out did not fit into what they knew or thought was correct. So they changed their "ideas" until the new piece of knowledge fitted. These truth trailers are still at work, finding out new things, rejecting the old incorrect ideas, and trying to solve the big mystery of the universe.

In this work we can describe only a few of the great achievements of these men and women. There are hundreds of astronomers at work this very minute, spreading light in dark places and making the world a more interesting place in which to live.

THALES

The Man Who Knew How to Foretell an Eclipse

(640–546 B.C.)

WE ARE not certain he was Greek. Some say he was a Phoenician, but we do know that he traveled in Egypt and in Babylonia, because it was only in these places that he could have learned the things he knew. The historians tell us that he predicted the eclipse of the sun that took place the day of the battle between the Lydians and Medes. That was on May 28, 585 B.C. We can be sure of the date because the astronomer can figure out just when that eclipse did take place. Histories tell us that the warriors were so frightened that they forgot to fight and called off the battle. This is one way the scientist can help the historians, by checking up his dates.

Thales also could find the height of the Pyramids by measuring their shadows. You can do the same thing with a tree or a flagpole (see Chapter VII). It is a somewhat similar scheme the astronomers use to get the distance to the moon or sun or even the nearest star.

There are a lot of things Thales did not know, too. He thought the world was flat. Most people thought so and did not know it was a great big ball. You know better than that and can prove it (see Chapter V). Nevertheless, Thales was a great man and for his day made great advances in knowledge. He not only enjoyed learning about things but he liked to make use of his knowledge. He even tried to measure the size of the sun and to get the exact length of the year.

HIPPARCHUS

Who First Wrote Down the Stars

(146–126 B.C.)

THIS old Greek scientist must have known the stars very well because in 134 B.C. he was surprised to see a new one in the sky. It surprised him, but it would not shock us. It happens every few years and we call them "novae." Hipparchus decided that if these were to be additions to the sky (he did not know that "new stars" are only temporary and soon fade), he should make a list or map of the sky. This he did (Chapter V gives a scheme for roughly doing this). He catalogued over 1,000 stars.

Ptolemy used this catalogue and brought it up to date in such a way that we started with his work. Many other catalogues have been made since. All that we know of the Hipparchus catalogue has come to us through Ptolemy.

Hipparchus also discovered another important thing that was not explained until Sir Isaac Newton trailed the truth to this great puzzle. It is called "the precession of the equinoxes," but we cannot explain it here; it is too long a story. The place where the sun is on March 21, called the "vernal equinox," moves around the sky very slowly. It takes nearly 26,000 years to go once around. That makes each year a few seconds shorter than it should be. Hipparchus noticed this but did not know why. Don't you think he was pretty smart to even find such a little difference?

PTOLEMY

He Believed the Sun Went around the Earth

(A.D. 100–178)

IN EGYPT 1,800 years ago, Ptolemy was as common a name as Smith or Brown is now. We do not know much about Ptolemy's parents or of what race he was. He lived at Alexandria where the great library was because he said, "We make our observations in the parallel of Alexandria." All his writings date between A.D. 127 and 151 so we just guessed at the dates above. Ptolemy was really interested in geography, and in measuring the size of the earth, and drawing the lines of latitude and longitude. So he had to use astronomy. But the thing he is most remembered for is a bad guess he made. Hs should not be blamed too much because there was really no way in which he could find out the truth. He had to choose between believing either that the earth went around the sun or that the sun went around the earth. He said the earth was the center of the system of sun, moon, and planets, and even the stars.

Of course that is wrong as you either know or will learn later (see Chapter VI). This was not his own idea. Hipparchus had preached it 300 years before and Ptolemy just repeated it. He was not even original enough to make his own mistakes. For 1,400 years his wrong guess was gospel. It was Copernicus who really set up a new scheme—the one that is generally accepted today.

COPERNICUS

Who Put the Earth in Its Place

(1473–1543)

THIS great man was a Polish monk, modest, kindhearted, and very religious, but he did not give a rap for the opinions of other people. He studied the old Greek writers and some of them did not agree with Hipparchus, who believed that the earth was the center of the universe. Neither did Nicholas Copernicus. For more than 35 years, he thought about the matter and then he made up his mind. He would publish a book! People, of course, like to think they are important. To tell them that they were not at the hub of this universe, but merely on a little globe flying around the sun, was insulting and dangerous. He probably thought as much about that as he did about astronomy.

This book came like a bombshell and from the day it was printed until now it has displaced the ideas of Ptolemy. The book really did not prove anything. It merely reasoned so clearly that you could not argue against it. It was printed in Nuremberg, Germany, and had a very big name. The book was written in Latin and of course its name was long: *De revolutionibus orbium coelestium* or *About the Revolution of the Celestial Bodies*.

This book might have put Copernicus on the spot except for the fact that the first copy to come off the printing press was placed in his hands as he was dying, and through that book his soul goes marching on.

TYCHO BRAHE

Keen-eyed Searcher of the Sky

(1546–1601)

ON NOVEMBER 11, 1572, this Danish noble-man was startled by seeing a "new star" in Cassiopeia. He rubbed his eyes and asked the coachman if *he* could see it. He could, so then and there Tycho decided to be an astronomer. He was, no doubt, a student of the stars before or he would not have recognized this as a new star. He watched it night after night until it grew brighter than Jupiter. And then it faded from sight but not from memory because Tycho had recorded carefully all he saw and then wrote a book the next year: *De nova stella* or *The New Star*.

Tycho was a hotheaded young fellow. He fought a duel once and lost his nose as well as the duel. But he made an artificial one and wore it the rest of his life.

The King of Denmark, Frederick II, took a liking to this strange man and built him a $100,000 observatory and paid him a large pension to be a court astronomer. The observa-tory was called Oraniborg (The Castle of the Skies) and was the finest then known. Of course they had no telescopes, but they did have quadrants and astrolabes and cross-staffs (see Chapter V). This fellow was not so smart but he had good eyes and was a careful observer. He did not believe the Copernican theory and tried to make one of his own, a cross between Ptolemy's and Copernicus'. But it never worked and is now almost forgotten.

After 20 years, the king died, politics changed, and out went Tycho. He went over to Prague, Bohemia, where Rudolph II set him up again. He carried with him all his records, and here he made more. Then Johannes Kepler, a young man, came along to help him. He died with all his work unfinished—and the rest of the story really belongs to Kepler.

JOHANNES KEPLER

Whose Laws Govern the Planets

(1571–1630)

JOHANNES was offered a job as professor of astronomy and took it, even though he knew little about it. He really did not have to—it was sort of astrology, a fortune-telling job. He did not know one star from another, but he got down to it and began to learn. Unlike Tycho Brahe, with whom he was to do most of his work, he had vision and imagination. He liked to draw conclusions, but he was poor on observations—and that's where he teamed up with Tycho, who was just the opposite—long on looking, short on thinking.

When he was about twenty-four years old, he found a trick that he thought would solve all the problems of the planets' motions. After working hard at it, he published it—and now it is just a curiosity. But it was the open sesame for Johannes. A copy of it fell into Tycho's hands and that exiled Dane sent for the young man to come to Prague as his assistant. So he packed up the family and off they went to a strange place. There Tycho and Kepler worked in a friendly, pleasant way. Tycho died but Kepler promised to carry on their work.

He worked over the stack of observations Tycho had piled up and found queer things in the writings. Things that would not work out with the planets moving around the sun in circles. Suppose they don't? That's an idea! Try ellipses. The problem is solved! The planets move in ellipses around the sun (see Chapter VI). Then he set to and published the star lists of Tycho—with Rudolph's money. In 1627 Rudolph's Tables were on sale. Kepler's work was over. The world knew *how* the planets moved but not *why*. That was Newton's job.

★ 230 ★

GALILEO GALILEI

Who First Turned the Telescope to the Stars

(1564-1642)

THIS Italian mathematician and astronomer was a very ingenious fellow and tried many tricks to find out things, but his important gift to us was his curiosity. He heard about a strange contrivance of lenses with which distant objects might be seen as clearly as those at hand. Many people had looked through this tube with lenses at the ends and marveled that the church steeple looked so close. But no one ever bothered to look at the stars. Then Galileo heard about it and made one. That is how the boys made radio sets from 1915 to 1930.

He looked at the Milky Way and found it was made up of great star clouds. Nobody knew that before. The moon was easy. There he saw ranges of mountains and peaks by the hundreds. He also saw great smooth-looking dark spots and they looked so much like water that he called them *maria* which means seas. (Chapter X will tell you more than Galileo ever knew about the moon.) Venus looked like the crescent moon (see Chapter X) and that startled him. Near Jupiter he saw four little stars in a row. Each night they were in a different place but always close to this giant planet and in a line. They were not stars! He had discovered four of Jupiter's nine moons and it did not take him long to get the idea. This was just like the solar system Copernicus had described!

He proudly went around telling about his discoveries and even wrote a book about them, but it got him into a great deal of trouble with his church. So he took it all back—said he was wrong—but he kept his fingers crossed while he said it. He studied gravity (you know about the story of dropping a ball from the Leaning Tower at Pisa) and got together the material that Newton used later in his work on *why* the planets move as they do.

★ 231 ★

ISAAC NEWTON

Whose Mind Made the Universe One Big Family

(1642–1727)

 THIS Englishman was a peculiar chap. He did not get along so well at school, but he speeded up when he had an interest in science. He was ingenious when a lad. He made sundials (you can, too, in Chapter VIII) and studied wind pressure by jumping with and against the wind. Not a very scientific way to do it, but he had fun trying to learn things.

Everybody has heard the apple story. Maybe it is true, and maybe not—anyhow it is a good story. Newton once saw an apple fall, and he thought the attraction of the earth had caused it. The same pull that made the apple fall perhaps kept the moon from flying away from the earth. That was it! Just like a sling or the water that stays in the pail when you swing it around. He grabbed a piece of paper and his fountain pen (maybe he did not have a fountain pen) and worked it out. Wrong! Here is the queer thing about Newton. Instead of mulling over it and trying to find the trouble, he put it away for seven years.

The next thing that attracted him was the making of a better telescope. When he got it working, the view was bad. He started on a new tack and made a mirror telescope. Now you can make small ones like Newton made (see Chapter IX), and many thousands of dollars are now being spent on the great 200-inch mirror just like Isaac's 1-inch telescope.

In 1672 he got out his old apple problem and solved it. He had the earth the wrong size. Now it was easy. So he worked more and more on gravity. He explained Kepler's work. He even went back to Hipparchus and solved his problems. All this and more went with the greatest book on science ever written, the *Principia* or *Principles*. In that, one great principle ties the whole universe together and, strange to say, his principle itself is not even in his book!

OLAUS ROMER
Who First Clocked the Speed of Light
(1644–1710)

 THIS great Dane was working at the Paris Observatory when he made a discovery that settled a great argument. There were some who said that light traveled over space instantly. It seems that way, doesn't it? It was simply too fast for anyone to measure so almost everybody concluded it had no speed. There are always a few doubters around. Galileo tried to measure the speed, but he was too slow to catch it so he thought along with the crowd. I don't know whether Römer thought it had a speed or not, but it makes no difference. The discovery was thrown at him and he caught it!

He was studying the motion of one of the four moons Galileo had found accompanying Jupiter. He would figure out when the little moon would be eclipsed in Jupiter's shadow—and he was wrong so often that it worried him. He checked over all his work—and then! It might be that when Jupiter and the earth were on the same side of the sun and we were close to the giant planet, the eclipses would be early. When we're way on the opposite side, they would be late.

He tried out his trick, and there it was! Light did have a speed. It was something about 186,000 miles a second. Now that is one of the most important numbers in all astronomy. He did not find the speed very accurately but it was enough to even find it had one. That was in 1675 and since then many trials have been made. Each year tests are improved. Professor A. A. Michelson devoted almost his whole life to this one problem. Light, the highway we use to visit the stars, and think how fast we can travel it!

EDMUND HALLEY

Who First Foretold a Comet's Coming

(1656–1742)

COMETS have always had bad reputations. Were there not plagues and fires and wars in the years that had these flaming visitors in the sky? How could anyone suppose they were merely astronomical bodies like the moon or planets? And get this: the young Englishman thought so! He was a student of celestial mechanics and had sent his first paper to the Royal Society when he was only nineteen. He had found a new way to compute the orbits of the planets.

On the strength of this he figured out that Venus would cross over the face of the sun in 1761 and announced it in 1716. He had a better scheme for finding the distance to the sun from this "transit." Someone else did observe it, as Edmund Halley had died nineteen years before Venus actually did cross the face of the sun just as he had predicted.

Even more startling was the study he gave comets. He said they moved around the sun in ellipses just as the planets move. That was Kepler's discovery. He looked up all the old comet records and found out that the one which had been visible in 1682 was an old friend and regular visitor. It had been visible in 1607, 1531, 1456, and 1305. According to Halley, the same old comet is visiting us every 75 years or so. It seems they missed its visit in 1380 but it was there all right. Then he predicted it would come back in 1758, and it did. We saw it in 1910—the same old Halley comet—and you can look for it about 1985 and it will be here. Halley was right!

JAMES BRADLEY
Whose Failure Spelled Success

(1693–1762)

MANY people had said that if Copernicus was right and the earth did go around the sun, the stars should all move first one way and then the other, as the earth swung around its orbit. A few tried to measure this motion but failed. Then came Jim Bradley and his friend Sam Molyneux. Bradley was a preacher with a flare for astronomy. They built a vertical telescope up a chimney in Sam's house, and then went down cellar to watch the stars sail overhead. One of their favorites was γ Draconis (see page 82) and whether you believe it or not, they could see it in the daytime in their telescope.

They expected it to swing back and forth in the course of a year but it fooled them. It swung back and forth all right, but in the wrong direction. It reached the ends of its swing in March and September. It should be between June and December. They were seeing the earth swing around its orbit. They were not measuring the distance to a star. This was not parallax. This was something new! What was it? Bradley looked at Molyneux and Molyneux looked at Bradley. So they went upstairs to think it over. Still no answer.

One day Jim went out sailing and there he saw the flag in the boat blowing this way and that. The sailors could explain that easily. It was the combined motion of the boat and wind. Back to the cellar quick! That motion of the stars was a combination of the motion of the earth and the motion of light. And "aberration" was discovered! Is it any wonder such a clever person became a professional astronomer later—and then discovered some other things? But as Kipling said, "That's another story."

★ 235 ★

FRIEDRICH WILHELM BESSEL

Who First Found the Distance to a Star

(1784–1846)

 "How far away are the stars?" That question had been asked for thousands of years before the answer came. If Ptolemy had known, he might have guessed better about the motion of the earth and sun. Kepler did not know. Newton even let the problem pass. Bradley tried to discover the secret and found something equally as important. The man who first answered the question was Bessel—and that was in 1838, about 100 years ago! And then two others did it at the same time!

The scheme he used is simple (you can do it in Chapter V.) To do it he had to measure a very small angle. Which star would be a good one to start on? He must find one that is relatively close. But he found one in Cygnus, the Swan (see Chapter II), known as 61 Cygni. He had to measure an angle of 0.31 seconds. It takes nearly 4,000,000 of such angles to make a complete circle.

This is hard to do with everything at rest. But the earth is spinning like a great top all the time—and going around the sun, which is moving daily with the planets (see Chapter VI). So it gave Bessel quite a problem. He measured this not once but thousands of times over a period of three years. Then there was computing; sheet after sheet of numbers and the answer: "61 Cygni is 62,310,000,000,000 miles away"! That is 670,000 times as far away as the sun, yet one of the closest stars we can see from the United States. This is not all that Bessel did. He believed he detected Sirius (the Dog Star) to be double but it took young Alvan Clark, many years later, to "see" it. He worked on comets and solved other long and involved problems.

JOHN COUCH ADAMS

Who Discovered the Planet Neptune

(1819–1892)

IF YOU are a very keen-eyed observer, you can see ε Lyrae as two stars instead of one (see Lyra—Chapter II). Imagine half of the distance between those stars and you will know how far out of its figured place Uranus was about 1840. Even that little bit bothered this young man in England. John wanted to explain it; he believed it was caused by the gravity pull of another planet even farther away from the sun than Uranus. After working on the problem, and I suppose getting a few headaches, he figured out where this new brother to the earth should be. Now comes the rub! He had no telescope. He could not look for it himself so he sent his work to his old professor-friend Challis. He had a telescope but no good star map. He looked and actually found the new planet but did not recognize it; he thought it was a star. After some weeks' delay, he sent the work to the Royal Observatory at Greenwich. But they were so busy that they forgot it and kept it a year, safe in a pigeonhole of the desk. Then they sent it back to Challis and said, "Hunt for it." He did, but still did not recognize it as a planet. It is so small that it really looks like a star.

Meanwhile a Frenchman, Leverrier, had calculated it just as Adams had done. Neither knew about the other's work (honestly, they didn't). But he sent his story to Berlin, to Galle at the observatory there. They were all set to do the work, and in less than an hour a new planet had been added to the sun's family. Who gets the credit?

HENRIETTA M. LEAVITT

Keen-eyed Measurer of Space

(1868–1921)

THIS famous American astronomer dis-covered a means of measuring distance that is one of the most valuable weapons of the modern astronomer. By means of her clever trick we can measure distances to stars that are so great that we cannot even see the stars! As long as we can get its picture, we can work the trick if the star is of the right sort. But let's start the story at the beginning.

When she was studying some pictures of the lesser Magel-lanic Cloud (that is, the great cluster of stars down near the south pole of the sky), Miss Leavitt noticed something strange that no one else had ever seen. Some of the stars did not have steady light but they flickered. What she noticed was that the dimmer the star was, the faster it blinked. This great cloud of stars is so far away that, even though the stars were scattered somewhat, it was safe to say they were all at the same distance.

This kind of star was an old story. Many had been spotted on the sky but no one knew there was any relation between their flickering period and their real brightness (the as-tronomer calls this "luminosity"). But there was, and Miss Leavitt found it. She made up a table that told how bright any of these variable stars actually were, if you knew their periods. That is the period-luminosity law.

If you can see a star flicker on a set of pictures taken, say, every five hours for several days, you know its "real" bright-ness. You can measure how bright it looks and then a little figuring will tell you its distance—and it makes no difference whether it is one light-year away or 10,000,000. The scheme is good, isn't it? It makes Bessel a stay-at-home with his parallax method!

WILLIAM, CAROLINE, AND JOHN HERSCHEL

A Famous Star-minded Family

THIS trio is famous for many things. William (1738–1822) was a German by birth and a musician. When he was still a young man he went to England, led a church choir, and played the organ. Soon his sister Caroline (1750–1848) joined him. His interest in the stars grew, and he wanted a telescope. He had no spare money to buy one, so he made one. Then another and another, each larger and better than the one before. His fame grew and people bought his instruments. Meanwhile Caroline kept his house and learned astronomy and mathematics. Then she began observing and working problems for William when he was working with his singers. Sometimes he worked on his mirrors (like those described in Chapter IX, only of metal) for as much as 16 hours at a time and Caroline fed him so he would not lose a stroke.

One night William found a new world—Uranus. He named it Georgium Sidus—George's Star—for the king. The French insisted on calling it Herschel, but everyone now calls it Uranus. Caroline was good at finding comets. She picked up five.

William married and his son John (1792–1871) became a pioneer in the Southern Hemisphere. His aunt Caroline went off to live alone, but kept in close touch with her nephew's important work at the observatory. He set up at the Cape of

Good Hope. He extended his father's catalogue of nebulae and clusters to the southern sky.

It was William Herschel who first found out that the sun was moving through space, carrying the planet along (see Chapter VI). He even found the direction it was going and something about its speed. It was John's plan that Bessel used in finding parallax.

ADVANCED READING ACTIVITY

Frost, E. B.: *An Astronomer's Life*. Boston, Houghton Mifflin Company, 1933.

Lowell, Lawrence: *Biography of Percival Lowell*. New York, The Macmillan Company, 1935.

Newcomb, Simon: *Reminiscences of an Astronomer*.

Williams, H. S.: *The Great Astronomers*. New York, Simon & Schuster, Inc., 1930.

Wilson, Grove: *Great Men of Science*. Garden City, N. Y., Garden City Publishing Company, 1929.

Do You Know?

1. That our sun is the "nearest" star, 93,000,000 miles away?

2. That we see one side only of the moon?

3. That we see more of Venus at the crescent phase than when it is nearly full?

4. That the "man" and "woman" in the moon are its "seas"?

5. That the moon is not a smooth disk but as rough as the mountains on the earth?

6. That crooners, opera singers, and radios would not jar you on the moon because there is no atmosphere to carry sound to your ears?

7. That if you weighed 90 pounds here you would weigh only 15 on the moon?

8. That no baseball pitcher could throw a curve or drop for the same reason?

9. That a champion sprinter could run the hundred-yard dash in about two seconds on the moon?

10. That the "brain trust," 200 years before Christ, taught that the earth was a spinning globe?

11. That the sun is sometimes fast by 16½ minutes and again slow by 14½ minutes reaching high noon?

12. That ice manufacturers on Jupiter and Saturn could get ammonia for nothing from the atmosphere?

13. That the planet Uranus was the first ever "discovered," and its discoverer, Herschel, was supposed to receive an annuity of about $1,000 per year?

14. That E. E. Barnard built his home from money prizes which he won discovering comets and he called it the House that Comets Built?

15. That every star we see is "passing light" and "past time"?

16. That Betelgeuse, the shoulder star in Orion, is 27,000,-000 times larger than the sun?

17. That a faint companion star to Sirius, in Canis Major, is composed of material so heavy that a baseball made of it would weigh 12 tons?

18. That the world is closer to the sun on New Year's Day than on the Fourth of July?

19. That our spring and summer are a week longer than autumn and winter?

20. That the moon should look smaller on the horizon than when it is overhead, but actually looks larger?

21. That a comet's tail always travels ahead of it when it begins to move away from the sun?

22. That "shooting stars" and "falling stars" are not stars at all?

23. That nothing has been found in a meteorite which has not already been known on earth?

24. That we never see Venus, but only the "veil" of clouds around it?

25. That Mars has polar caps very much like those on the earth?

26. That the Andromeda Nebula is the farthest object you can see without a telescope?

27. That Galileo was the first to use the telescope on the stars, but that he did not invent it?

28. That we would have to find 1,300 worlds to fill Jupiter?

29. That the nearest "fixed" star to us is 277,000 times farther out in space than the sun?

30. That the stars shine in the daytime as well as at night and that we cannot see them because the sun blots them out?

31. That the stars which you see during winter nights are in the sky during the summer days?

32. That the planet Venus can be seen in broad daylight?

ADVANCED READING ACTIVITY

Johnson, Gaylord: *The Stars for Children*. New York, The Macmillan Company, 1936.

Lockwood, Marian, and Arthur L. Draper: *The Earth among the Stars*. New York, Basic Books, Inc., 1935.

Olcott, W. T.: *Star Lore of All Ages*. New York, G. P. Putnam's Sons, 1936.

Olcott, W. T.: *Sun Lore of All Ages*. New York, G. P. Putnam's Sons, 1936.

Reed, W. Maxwell: *The Stars for Sam*. New York, Harcourt, Brace and Company, 1935.

Wylie, C. C.: *Astronomy, Maps and Weather*. New York, Harper & Brothers, 1942.

Index

Pronunciation is indicated by marking the long vowels. Others are short. The marks indicate the following sounds: ā as in āpe, ē as in mē, ī as in Īce, ō as in gō, ū as in rūle, ōō as in bōōt. Different authorities give different pronunciations for the proper names used in astronomy. When in doubt refer to a good dictionary.

Boldface numbers indicate the pages of important references.
Italic numbers indicate pages with photographs or drawings.

N

Navigation, 97
  thumbnail, 111–118
    maps for, 112
    month correction table for, 117
Nebulae, *21, 31, 33, 37, 39, 43, 45, 49, 57, 63, 65, 37, 71,* 79, 199
Neptune, 8, 127, 128, 144, 237
New General Catalogue, 17
New star (*see* Nova)
Newton, Isaac, Sir (1642–1727, 123, **232**
North Star (*see* Polaris)
Nova, 9, 25, 61, *69,* 229

O

Octant, 100, 101
Ophiuchus (of-i-ū′kus), *37,* 82
Orion (ō-rī′-on), 11, 26, 37, 74, **78,** 81, *206*
  α, β, ζ Orionis (ō-ri-ō′nis), 79
Orionids (o-rī′on-idz), 94
Orrery, 126

P

Parallax, 145
Parsec, 145
Pegasus (peg′a-sus), 45, 71, 72, 83
  α, β, π, ε Pegasi (peg′a-sī), 73
Period-luminosity law, 238
Perseids (pur′se-idz), 94, *223*
Perseus (per′sūs), 11, 18, 52, **68**
  β, η Persei (per-se′i), 69
Pisces (pis′ēz), 11, 26, **44**
  α, ζ Piscium (pis′i-um), 45
Piscis Austrinus (pis′is aw-strī′nus), 74
Planetarium, Hayden (hā′den), 61, 125
Planets, 8, 47, 127, **128,** 195–198, 213
  positions (1946–1949), 132–135
Pleiades (plī′a-dēz), 49
Pluto (plōō′to), 8, 51, 127, 128, 144

Pointers, 21
Polaris (po-lār′is), 23, 97, *98,* 146, 220
Polestar (*see* Polaris)
Pollux (pol′uks), **51,** 146
Praesepe (pre-sē′pē), 29
Principia (prin-sip′i-a), 232
Procyon (prō′si-on), **81,** 146
Ptolemy (tol′e-mi) (100–178), 6, 29, 121, 227
Puppis (pup′pis), 74

Q

Quadrant, *99,* 101, 103, *105*
Quadrantids (kwod′ran-tidz), 94
Queen on the Throne, 25

R

Ram, **46,** 49
Regulus (reg′ū-lus), **31,** 49, 146
Retrogression, 131
Rigel (rē′jel), **79,** 146, 206
Right ascension (R.A.), 113–118
Rittenhouse, David (rit′n-hous) (1732–1796), 126
Rival of Mars, 37
Römer, Olaus (ru′mer) (1644–1710), 144, **233**
Ronchi test (ron′chi), 182
Rosse, William Parsons, Third Earl of (ros) (1800–1867), 43

S

Sagitta (sa-jit′a), 82
Sagittarius (saj-i-tā′ri-us), 11, 26, **38,** 41
  μ Sagittarii (saj-i-tā′ri-ī), 39
Saiph, (sa′iph′), 206
Saturn (sat′urn), 8, 45, 127, 128, 130–136, 144, 198, 213
Scales, 35
Scheat (shē-at′), 147
Schedar (shā′der), 25, 146
Scorpius (skor′pi-us), 11, 26, 35, **36**
  α, β, ν Scorpii (skor′pi-ī), 37

★ 249 ★